INSIDE

LANGUAGE · LITERACY · CONTENT

Acknowledgments

Grateful acknowledgment is given to the authors, artists, photographers, museums, publishers, and agents for permission to reprint copyrighted material. Every effort has been made to secure the appropriate permission. If any omissions have been made or if corrections are required, please contact the Publisher.

Photographic Credits

Cover (front): Leafcutter Bee on Fishhook Barrel Cactus Blossom, Sonoran Desert, Arizona, USA, John Cancalosi. Photograph © John Cancalosi/Peter Arnold/Getty Images.

Acknowledgments continue on page 191.

For product information and technology asistance, contact us at **Cengage Learning Customer & Sales Support, 1-800-354-9706**

For permission to use material from this text or product, submit all requests online at **www.cengage.com/permissions**
Further permissions questions can be emailed to **permissionrequest@cengage.com**

National Geographic Learning | Cengage Learning
1 Lower Ragsdale Drive
Building 1, Suite 200
Monterey, CA 93940

Cengage Learning is a leading provider of customized learning solutions with office locations around the globe, including Singapore, the United Kingdom, Australia, Mexico, Brazil, and Japan. Locate your local office at **www.cengage.com/global**.

Visit National Geographic Learning online at **ngl.cengage.com**
Visit our corporate website at **www.cengage.com**

Printer: RR Donnelley, Harrisonburg, VA

ISBN: 978-12857-34712 (Practice Book)
ISBN: 978-12857-34668 (Practice Book Teacher's Annotated Edition)

ISBN: 978-12857-67963 (Practice Masters)
Teachers are authorized to reproduce the practice masters in this book in limited quantity and solely for use in their own classrooms.

Printed in the United States of America
15 16 17 18 19 20 21 22
10 9 8 7 6 5 4 3

PRACTICE BOOK

Teacher's Annotated Edition

INSIDE

LANGUAGE · LITERACY · CONTENT

Contents

Foundations of Reading

Unit 1

Unit 2

Unit 2, continued

Unit 3

Unit 4

Contents, continued

Unit 5

Unit 6

Unit 7

Unit 7, continued

Foundations of Reading

▶ Letters and Sounds

A. Study the new letters and sounds.

Ss
seed

Mm
map

Ff
fish

Hh
hand

Tt
tiger

Aa
apple

B. Say the name of each picture below. What letter spells the <u>first</u> sound you hear? Circle the letter.

1.

t   (h)   a
hall

4.

f   h   (a)
astronaut

7.

a   m   (t)
tape

2.

a   h   (s)
soap

5.

a   (m)   s
mask

8.

a   s   (m)
mouse

3.

h   (f)   s
fence

6.

t   h   (a)
ant

9.

(t)   h   a
tiger

Foundations of Reading

► Letters and Sounds

Say the name of each picture below. What letter spells the <u>first</u> sound you hear? Write the letter.

1.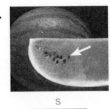

s

seed

2.

t

ten

3.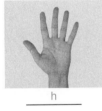

h

hand

4.

s

sandwich

5.

a

apple

6.

m

map

7.

h

helmet

8.

t

tape

9.

f

fish

10.

f

fence

11.

a

ant

12.

a

astronaut

13.

m

mouse

14.

f

fan

15.

s

six

Name _____

► High Frequency Words

Read each word. Then write it.

1. am _____ *am*   4. school _____ *school*

2. I _____ *I*   5. the _____ *the*

3. is _____ *is*   6. this _____ *this*

How to Play

1. Make a spinner.

2. Write the name of each player on a blank.

3. Spin. Read the sentence.

The first player to read all six sentences wins.

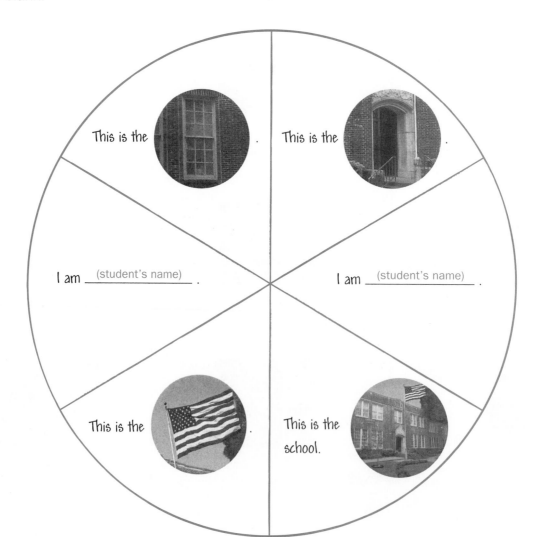

Foundations of Reading

► High Frequency Words

Read each word. Then write it.

1. a _____ a _____   4. my _____ my _____

2. an _____ an _____   5. no _____ no _____

3. here _____ here _____   6. you _____ you _____

---

1. Find the words. Circle them.
   Look across. ➡

q	(a)	o	p	t	m
v	l	e	s	(a	n)
s	b	m	l	n	l
(h	e	r	e)	o	r
z	p	l	g	(m	y)
(n	o)	r	z	q	w
w	f	(y	o	u)	z
x	g	q	t	d	s

5. Find the words. Circle them.
   Look down. ⬇

a	q	h	j	z	t
n	v	e	u	n	s
k	s	r	r	o	g
l	b	e	h	o	y
r	(a)	i	z	e	o
x	f	s	m	r	u
w	g	o	y	e	q
p	u	z	e	l	v

Write the missing words.

2. Here is _____ my _____  .
   (my / no)

3. Here is _____ a _____  .
   (you / a)

4. _____ Here _____ is a  .
   (A / Here)

Write the missing words.

6. This is _____ an _____ .
   (an / you)

7. _____ Here _____ is a .
   (Here / My)

8. This is _____ a _____ 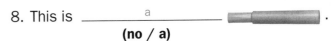 .
   (no / a)

Name _____

▶ High Frequency Words

A. Read each word. Then write it.

1. at	_____at_____	4. of	_____of_____	
2. it	_____it_____	5. on	_____on_____	
3. look	_____look_____	6. yes	_____yes_____	

B. Write the missing letters.

7. Which words have a **t**?

_a_ _t_   _i_ _t_

8. Which words have 2 letters?

_a_ _t_   _o_ _f_

_i_ _t_   _o_ _n_

9. Which word has 3 letters?

_y_ _e_ _s_

10. Which word has 4 letters?

_l_ _o_ _o_ _k_

11. Which words start with **o**?

_o_ _f_   _o_ _n_

12. Which word has an **f**?

_o_ _f_

C. Write the missing words.

13. Carlos, _____look_____ at this!
    (of / look)

14. Is this the school?
    Yes, _____it_____ is.
    (it / at)

15. I am _____at_____ school.
    (at / of)

16. This is a _____of_____
    (of / look)
    the school.

17. The is _____on_____
    (it / on)
    the .

Name _____

▶ **Read on Your Own**

Read these sentences.

Sam has ham.

Sam has a hat.

Sam has a mat.

Foundations of Reading

Name _____

▶ Words with Short *a*

A. Read each word. Draw a line to match the word and the picture.

1.

hat

ham

2.

fat ─────────

mat ─────────

B. Write the missing words.

3.

This is a _____hat_____ .
   (ham / hat)

6.

I _____am_____ Ron.
   (Sam / am)

4.

Maylin is ___at___ school.
   (at / sat)

7.

This is a _____ham_____ .
   (ham / hat)

5.

Here is the ___mat___ .
   (fat / mat)

8.

You ___sat___ at the 🪑 .
   (at / sat)

Foundations of Reading

Name _____

▶ Words with Short *a*

A. Write the missing *a*. Then read the words in each list. How are the words different?

1.

     __a__ m

S __a__ m

h __a__ m

2.

__a__ t

h __a__ t

s __a__ t

3.

__a__ t

f __a__ t

m __a__ t

B. What word completes each sentence and tells about the picture? Spell the word.

4.

Here is my __h__ __a__ __t__ .

5.

I am __f__ __a__ __t__ .

6.

This is a __h__ __a__ __m__ .

7.

I am __a__ __t__ school.

8.

I __a__ __m__ Ron.

9.

I __s__ __a__ __t__ on the .

10.

Sam __h__ __a__ __s__ a .

11.

Look at the __m__ __a__ __t__ .

12.

I __a__ __m__ at the .

13.

You __s__ __a__ __t__ at the .

Foundations of Reading

▶ **Letters and Sounds**

A. Study the new letters and sounds.

Nn
newspaper

Ll
lamp

Pp
pizza

Gg
girl

Ii
invitation

B. Say the name of each picture below. What letter spells the <u>first</u> sound you hear? Circle the letter.

1.

(n)   f   s
nurse

2.

l   (p)   n
pin

3.

(s)   l   n
sandwich

4.

t   h   (i)
insect

5.
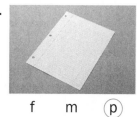

f   m   (p)
paper

6.

(g)   p   l
guitar

7.

p   (f)   i
fan

8.

l   (n)   t
notebook

9.

l   (p)   n
pan

10.

(l)   g   n
library

11.

t   (g)   a
girl

12.

(l)   g   f
light

Foundations of Reading

▶ Letters and Sounds

Say the name of each picture below. Write the missing letters.

1.

    <u>h</u> <u>a</u> <u>m</u>

2.

    <u>h</u> <u>a</u> <u>t</u>

3.

    <u>p</u> <u>i</u> <u>n</u>

4.

    <u>s</u> <u>i</u> <u>t</u>

5.

    <u>p</u> <u>i</u> <u>g</u>

6.

    <u>m</u> <u>a</u> <u>n</u>

7.

    <u>p</u> <u>a</u> <u>n</u>

8.

    <u>l</u> <u>a</u> <u>m</u> <u>p</u>

9.

    <u>f</u> <u>a</u> <u>n</u>

10.

    <u>m</u> <u>a</u> <u>t</u>

11.

    <u>h</u> <u>i</u> <u>t</u>

12.

    <u>m</u> <u>a</u> <u>p</u>

Name _____

► **High Frequency Words**

A. Read each word. Then write it.

1. are	_____are_____	4. show	_____show_____
2. good	_____good_____	5. where	_____where_____
3. see	_____see_____	6. he	_____he_____

B. Write the missing letters.

7. Which words have 4 letters?

   g̲ ̲ o̲ ̲ o̲ ̲ d̲

   s̲ ̲ h̲ ̲ o̲ ̲ w̲

8. Which word has an **a**?

   a̲ ̲ r̲ ̲ e̲

9. Which word has 5 letters?

   w̲ ̲ h̲ ̲ e̲ ̲ r̲ ̲ e̲

10. Which words have 3 letters?

    s̲ ̲ e̲ ̲ e̲

    a̲ ̲ r̲ ̲ e̲

11. Which word has a **g**?

    g̲ ̲ o̲ ̲ o̲ ̲ d̲

12. Which words have a **w**?

    w̲ ̲ h̲ ̲ e̲ ̲ r̲ ̲ e̲

    s̲ ̲ h̲ ̲ o̲ ̲ w̲

13. Which word has 2 letters?

    h̲ ̲ e̲

C. Write the missing word.

14. I _____see_____ two pens.
    (see / are)

15. Where _____are_____ the people?
    (are / he)

16. This is a _____good_____ sandwich.
    (good / see)

17. _____Show_____ me the motorcycle.
    (Show / Where)

18. _____Where_____ is the boy?
    (Show / Where)

19. We do not know who _____he_____
    is.   **(see / he)**

► **High Frequency Words**

A. Read each word. Then write it.

1. answer _____answer_____   4. time _____time_____

2. she _____she_____   5. who _____who_____

3. some _____some_____   6. your _____your_____

B. Write the missing letters.

7. Which word has 6 letters?

a n s w e r

8. Which words have an **m**?

t i m e

s o m e

9. Which words have 3 letters?

s h e

w h o

10. Which words have 4 letters?

t i m e

y o u r

s o m e

11. Which words have a **w**?

a n s w e r

w h o

12. Which word has a **y**?

y o u r

C. Write the missing word.

13. I write the _____answer_____ .
(answer / some)

14. _____She_____ is my friend.
(She / Your)

15. What _____time_____ is class?
(time / your)

16. _____Your_____ puppy is very cute.
(Your / Who)

17. I have _____some_____ homework.
(some / who)

18. _____Who_____ do you see?
(Who / She)

Foundations of Reading

Name _____

► High Frequency Words

A. Read each word. Then write it.

1. point _____ point _____   4. with _____ with _____

2. read _____ read _____   5. work _____ work _____

3. to _____ to _____   6. write _____ write _____

B. Write the missing letters.

7. Which words have 4 letters?

__r__ __e__ __a__ __d__

__w__ __o__ __r__ __k__

__w__ __i__ __t__ __h__

8. Which words have a **w**?

__w__ __i__ __t__ __h__

__w__ __o__ __r__ __k__

__w__ __r__ __i__ __t__ __e__

9. Which words have 5 letters?

__w__ __r__ __i__ __t__ __e__

__p__ __o__ __i__ __n__ __t__

10. Which word has a **k**?

__w__ __o__ __r__ __k__

11. Which words have an **r**?

__r__ __e__ __a__ __d__

__w__ __o__ __r__ __k__

__w__ __r__ __i__ __t__ __e__

C. Write the missing word.

12. I _____ read _____ a book.
    (read / point)

13. I _____ point _____ to the answer.
    (work / point)

14. Carlos will _____ write _____ on
    (write / with)
    the board.

15. I need _____ to _____ see you.
    (point / to)

16. I will go _____ with _____ Lisa to
    (with / read)
    the store.

17. Eli likes to _____ work _____ on
    (with / work)
    computers.

Name _____

▶ **Read on Your Own**

Read these sentences.

Tim has a lamp.

Here is his pan.

This is his pin.

Here is his lid.

This is Tim.

Foundations of Reading

Name _____

► **Words with Short *a* and *i***

A. Read each word. Draw a line to match the word and the picture.

1.

pan

map

man

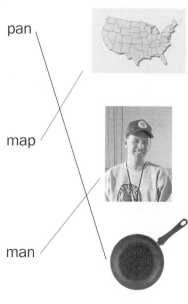

2.

pin

sit

pig

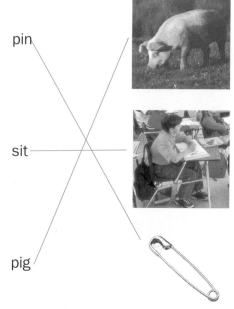

B. Write the missing words.

3.

She has a

____hat____ .

(hat / mat)

5.

This is a

____fan____ .

(fan / man)

7.

This is a

____pin____ .

(pin / pig)

9.

This is a

____pig____ .

(pan / pig)

4.

This is a

____ham____ .

(pan / ham)

6.

____Hit____ it!

(Pin / Hit)

8.

He is a

____man____ .

(man / mat)

10.

You

____sit____

(sit / hit)

in a .

F16

© NGSP & HB

Name _____

▶ Words with Short *a* and *i*

A. Write the missing letters. Then read the words in each list. How are the words different?

1.

 _h_ _a_ _m_

 _h_ _a_ _t_

 _m_ _a_ _t_

2.

 _p_ _a_ _n_

 _p_ _i_ _n_

 _p_ _i_ _g_

B. Read each question. What word goes in the answer? Spell the word. Then circle the correct picture.

3. Where is the pig?

The _p_ _i_ _g_ is here.

4. Where is the pan?

Here is the _p_ _a_ _n_ .

5. Where is Sam?

_S_ _a_ _m_ is here.

6. Who hit it?

Carlos _h_ _i_ _t_ it.

7. Who has the hat?

She _h_ _a_ _s_ the hat.

8. Who is the man?

He is the _m_ _a_ _n_ .

Foundations of Reading

► **Letters and Sounds**

A. Study the new letters and sounds.

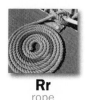
Rr
rope

Dd
desk

Cc
camel

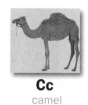
Vv
van

Oo
office

B. Say the name of each picture below. What letter spells the <u>first</u> sound you hear? Circle the letter.

1.

m   (d)   o
door

5.

c   n   (v)
video

9.

(r)   d   f
rice

13.

(c)   p   t
computer

2.

r   v   (n)
net

6.

o   r   (i)
insect

10.

a   (v)   l
vase

14.

o   m   (v)
vest

3.

l   h   (c)
calendar

7.

(l)   g   c
lamp

11.

(d)   a   s
dot

15.

(o)   d   i
ox

4.

a   (r)   d
ruler

8.

h   t   (p)
pan

12.

v   i   (h)
helmet

16.

d   (g)   v
guitar

Foundations of Reading

Name _____

▶ Letters and Sounds

Say the name of each picture below. Write the missing letters.

1.

d   o   t

2.

m   a   p

3.

p   o   t

4.

f   a   n

5.

v   a   n

6.

f   l   a   g

7.

c   l   a   s   s

8.

c   a   t

9.

r   a   g

10.

l   a   m   p

11.

p   i   g

12.

p   i   n

Name _____

► High Frequency Words

Read each word. Then write it.

1. do   <u>   do   </u>   4. help   <u>   help   </u>

2. does   <u>   does   </u>   5. in   <u>   in   </u>

3. for   <u>   for   </u>   6. like   <u>   like   </u>

How to Play

1. Play with a partner. 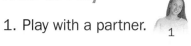 Each partner chooses a sign. X O

2. Partner 1 reads a word and marks the square with a sign.

3. Partner 2 takes a turn.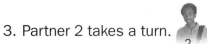

4. Get 3 **X**s or **O**s in a row to win.

A.

do	help	like
in	does	for
point	read	to

B.

does	point	read
in	do	help
for	like	to

C.

help	does	do
for	like	in
with	work	write

D.

like	work	does
write	do	help
for	with	in

Name _____

▶ **High Frequency Words**

A. Read each word. Then write it.

1. around	_____around_____	4. will	_____will_____
2. me	_____me_____	5. and	_____and_____
3. picture	_____picture_____	6. don't	_____don't_____

B. Write the missing letters.

7. Which word has 3 letters?

<u>a</u>   <u>n</u>   <u>d</u>

8. Which word is two words together?

<u>d</u>   <u>o</u>   <u>n</u>   <u>'</u>   <u>t</u>

9. Which word has 6 letters?

<u>a</u>   <u>r</u>   <u>o</u>   <u>u</u>   <u>n</u>   <u>d</u>

10. Which words have an **r**?

<u>a</u>   <u>r</u>   <u>o</u>   <u>u</u>   <u>n</u>   <u>d</u>

<u>p</u>   <u>i</u>   <u>c</u>   <u>t</u>   <u>u</u>   <u>r</u>   <u>e</u>

11. Which word has 2 letters?

<u>m</u>   <u>e</u>

12. Which words have a **d**?

<u>a</u>   <u>r</u>   <u>o</u>   <u>u</u>   <u>n</u>   <u>d</u>

<u>a</u>   <u>n</u>   <u>d</u>

<u>d</u>   <u>o</u>   <u>n</u>   <u>'</u>   <u>t</u>

C. Write the missing word.

13. I see your _____picture_____ in
    (picture / around)
    the yearbook.

14. Yes, I _____will_____
    (don't / will)
    play basketball.

15. Tell _____me_____ about
    (and / me)
    the game.

16. Can you run _____around_____
    (around / picture)
    the track?

17. Why _____don't_____ you
    (don't / and)
    stay there?

Foundations of Reading

▶ High Frequency Words

A. Read each word. Then write it.

1. food   _____food_____   4. both   _____both_____

2. not   _____not_____   5. get   _____get_____

3. that   _____that_____   6. these   _____these_____

B. Write the missing letters.

7. Which words have 3 letters?

n   o   t
___ ___ ___

g   e   t
___ ___ ___

8. Which words have 4 letters?

f   o   o   d
___ ___ ___ ___

t   h   a   t
___ ___ ___ ___

b   o   t   h
___ ___ ___ ___

9. Which words end in **t**?

n   o   t
___ ___ ___

g   e   t
___ ___ ___

t   h   a   t
___ ___ ___ ___

10. Which words have an **e**?

g   e   t
___ ___ ___

t   h   e   s   e
___ ___ ___ ___ ___

11. Which word has 5 letters?

t   h   e   s   e
___ ___ ___ ___ ___

C. Write the missing word.

12. I ate the ____food____ .
   (both / food)

13. Sam saw ____that____ apple.
   (get / that)

14. I did ____not____ see the
   (get / not)
   shooting star.

15. Did you ____both____ help
   (both / food)
   the girl?

16. Did Lin ____get____ the ball?
   (these / get)

17. We ate ____these____ chips.
   (food / these)

Name _____

▶ **Read on Your Own**

Read these sentences.

This dot is on a van.

The dot is on a map.

The dot is on a cot.

The dot is on a pig.

The dot is on Ron!

Foundations of Reading

Name _____

▶ Words with Short *a*, *i*, and *o*

A. Read each word. Draw a line to the correct picture.

1.

mop

map

man

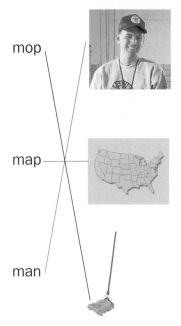

2.

pan

pig

pin

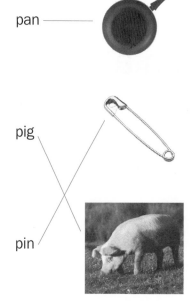

3.

pot

dot

mop

B. Write the missing words.

4.

This is a

_____van_____ .

(van / man)

5.

I like this

_____map_____ .

(map / man)

6.

The _____pot_____

(pot / dot)

is hot.

7.

Here is a good

_____mop_____ .

(map / mop)

8.

This is a

_____dot_____ .

(not / dot)

9.

This lamp is

_____on_____ .

(am / on)

Name _____

▶ Words with Short *a*, *i*, and *o*

A. Write the missing letters. Then read the words in each list. How are the words different?

1.

  <u>c</u> <u>o</u> <u>t</u>

  <u>d</u> <u>o</u> <u>t</u>

 <u>p</u> <u>o</u> <u>t</u>

2.

  <u>p</u> <u>i</u> <u>n</u>

  <u>p</u> <u>a</u> <u>n</u>

  <u>v</u> <u>a</u> <u>n</u>

3.

  <u>h</u> <u>i</u> <u>t</u>

  <u>h</u> <u>a</u> <u>t</u>

  <u>h</u> <u>a</u> <u>m</u>

B. Read each question and the answer. Write the missing words. Then circle the correct picture.

4. Is this pot hot?

No, the <u>p</u> <u>o</u> <u>t</u> is not <u>h</u> <u>o</u> <u>t</u>.

5. Is this your cap?

Yes, it is my <u>c</u> <u>a</u> <u>p</u> .

6. Where is the mop?

The <u>m</u> <u>o</u> <u>p</u> is here.

7. Where can I sit?

You can <u>s</u> <u>i</u> <u>t</u> here.

8. Point to the dot.

The <u>d</u> <u>o</u> <u>t</u> is here!

9. Do you like the hat?

Yes, I like the <u>h</u> <u>a</u> <u>t</u> .

Foundations of Reading

► Letters and Sounds

Study the new letters and sounds.

Jj
jacket

Bb
book

Ww
window

Kk
key

Ee
egg

How to Play Bingo

1. Write the letters from the box. Write one letter in each square.

2. Then listen to the word your teacher reads.

3. Put a ⬭ on the letter that stands for the first sound in the word.

4. The first player to cover all the letters in a row is the winner.

Letters to Write

a	i	p
b	j	r
b	j	s
c	k	t
d	k	v
e	l	w
f	m	w
g	n	
h	o	

Words to Read

am	got	lot	top
bat	hit	mat	van
big	it	not	win
can	jam	on	wig
dot	jog	pin	
egg	kid	red	
fat	kit	sit	

Foundations of Reading

Name _____

► Letters and Sounds

Say the name of each picture below. Write the missing letters.

1.

p o t

5.

v e s t

9.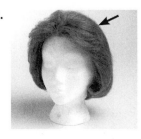

w i g

2.

r a g

6.

d o t

10.

k i t

3.

b a t

7.

v a n

11.

w e b

4.

e g g

8.

j o g

12.

d e s k

Foundations of Reading

▶ High Frequency Words

A. Read each word. Then write it.

1. things   _____things_____   4. them   _____them_____

2. little   _____little_____   5. those   _____those_____

3. old   _____old_____   6. very   _____very_____

B. Write the missing letters.

7. Which word has 3 letters?

  o   l   d
 ___ ___ ___

8. Which words have an **i**?

  t   h   i   n   g   s
 ___ ___ ___ ___ ___ ___

  l   i   t   t   l   e
 ___ ___ ___ ___ ___ ___

9. Which word has a **v**?

  v   e   r   y
 ___ ___ ___ ___

10. Which words have 4 letters?

  t   h   e   m
 ___ ___ ___ ___

  v   e   r   y
 ___ ___ ___ ___

C. Write the missing word.

11. The food is _____very_____ good.
    (very / little)

12. Did you see _____those_____
    (things / those)
    bananas?

13. The flea was very _____little_____ .
    (them / little)

14. I saw _____them_____ at school.
    (them / very)

15. The _____old_____ dog liked
    (things / old)
    to sleep.

16. I have many _____things_____ .
    (those / things)

Foundations of Reading

▶ High Frequency Words

A. Read each word. Then write it.

1. think _____think_____
2. take _____take_____
3. give _____give_____
4. which _____which_____
5. can _____can_____
6. play _____play_____

B. Write the missing letters.

7. Which words have 4 letters?

   t a k e
   ___ ___ ___ ___

   g i v e
   ___ ___ ___ ___

   p l a y
   ___ ___ ___ ___

8. Which words have 5 letters?

   t h i n k
   ___ ___ ___ ___ ___

   w h i c h
   ___ ___ ___ ___ ___

9. Which word has a **g**?

   g i v e
   ___ ___ ___ ___

10. Which word has 3 letters?

    c a n
    ___ ___ ___

11. Which words have an **a**?

    c a n
    ___ ___ ___

    t a k e
    ___ ___ ___ ___

    p l a y
    ___ ___ ___ ___

C. Write the missing word.

12. I _____think_____ I know the
    (think / play)
    answer.

13. Juan _____can_____ run very fast.
    (which / can)

14. _____Take_____ your turn next.
    (Take / Which)

15. Can you _____play_____ baseball?
    (can / play)

16. _____Which_____ book is yours?
    (Take / Which)

17. Let's _____give_____ food to the
    (give / play)
    hamster.

Foundations of Reading

Name _____

▶ **High Frequency Words**

A. Read each word. Then write it.

1. too _____too_____ 4. have _____have_____

2. feel _____feel_____ 5. how _____how_____

3. has _____has_____ 6. put _____put_____

B. Write the missing letters.

7. Which words have 3 letters?

t o o

h a s

h o w

p u t

8. Which words have 4 letters?

f e e l

h a v e

9. Which words have an **h**?

h o w

h a s

h a v e

10. Which word ends with a **t**?

p u t

11. Which word has two **e**'s?

f e e l

C. Write the missing word.

12. She has brown hair, _____too_____ .
   (too / how)

13. Where did you _____put_____
   (how / put)
   the book?

14. Do you _____feel_____ sick today?
   (have / feel)

15. She _____has_____ a blue
   (has / have)
   backpack.

16. _____How_____ are you feeling
   (Have / How)
   today?

17. I _____have_____ two cookies.
   (how / have)

▶ Read on Your Own

Read these sentences.

Can Ken jog?

Ken can jog well.

Can Ken get his bat?

Ken can get his bat.

Can Ken rest?

No. Ken has no bed!

Name _____

▶ Words with Short *a, i, o,* and *e*

A. Read each word. Draw a line to the correct picture.

1.

jam

ham

hat

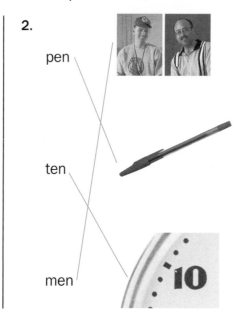

2.

pen

ten

men

3.

cat

bat

bed

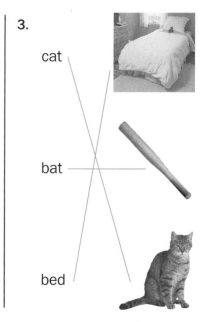

B. Write the missing words.

4.

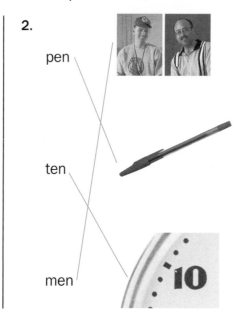

Here are two

_____men_____ .

(men / ten)

7.

This is a good

_____pen_____ .

(pan / pen)

10.

Here is a

_____bed_____ .

(bed / Ed)

5. ● ● ● ● ●
   ● ● ● ● ●

There are

_____ten_____ dots.

(ten / pen)

8.

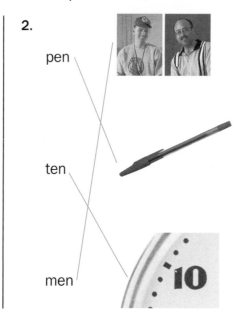

He can _____hit_____
(hot / hit)

the .

11.

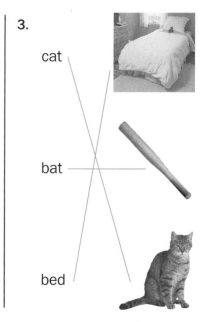

I do _____not_____
(dot / not)
like to play.

6.

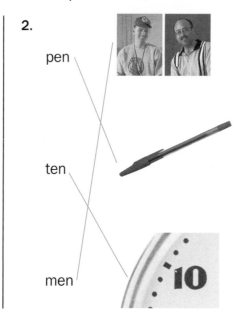

My pet is a

_____pig_____ .

(pig / pin)

9.

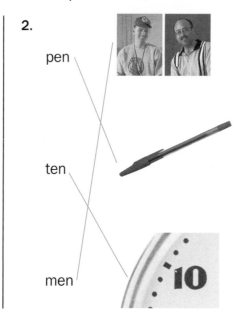

This is my

_____cap_____ .

(cap / map)

12.

Put it in the

_____pot_____ .

(pot / pat)

Foundations of Reading

Name _____

▶ Words with Short *a, i, o,* and *e*

A. Write the missing letters. Then read the words in each list. How are the words different?

1. m e n

 p e n

 t e n

2. c a t

 c o t

 p o t

3. p i n

 p i g

 w i g

B. Write the missing words.

4.

This is my p e n .

5.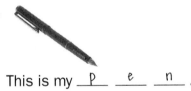

Look at the
w e b .

6.

Here is my b e d .

7.

Carlos has a
b a t .

8.

Do you like my
v e s t ?

9.

This is a
f l a g .

10.

I like to j o g .

11.

I s i t at my
desk.

12.

Where is my
n e t ?

Foundations of Reading

▶ Letters and Sounds

Study the new letters and sounds.

Zz
zero

Yy
yarn

Uu
umbrella

Qq
quarter

Xx
six

How to Play Bingo

1. Write the letters from the box. Write one letter in each square.

2. Then listen to the word your teacher reads.

3. Put a ◯ on the letter that stands for the first sound in the word.

4. The first player to cover all the letters in a row is the winner.

Letters to Write

a	j	s
b	k	t
c	l	u
d	m	v
e	n	w
f	o	y
g	p	z
h	q	
i	r	

Words to Read

am	him	on	van
bat	in	pen	wig
cot	jam	quit	yes
dot	kid	red	zip
egg	lot	sat	
fan	map	ten	
got	not	up	

Foundations of Reading

Name _____

▶ Letters and Sounds

Say the name of each picture below. Write the missing letters.

1.

l   e   g

2.

q   u   i   l   t

3.

a   x

4.

s   i   x

5.

c   u   p

6.

m   i   l   k

7.

r   u   g

8.

b   u   s

9.

u   p

10.

b   o   x

11.

s   u   n

12.

o   x

Name _____

▶ High Frequency Words

A. Read each word. Then write it.

1. they _____they_____
2. great _____great_____
3. later _____later_____
4. soon _____soon_____
5. tomorrow _____tomorrow_____
6. call _____call_____

B. Write the missing letters.

7. Which words have 4 letters?

t h e y

s o o n

c a l l

8. Which words have 5 letters?

g r e a t

l a t e r

9. Which words have an **a**?

g r e a t

l a t e r

c a l l

10. Which word ends with a **t**?

g r e a t

11. Which word has 8 letters?

t o m o r r o w

C. Write the missing word.

12. I will be in class _____tomorrow_____ .
(great / tomorrow)

13. I will see him _____soon_____ ,
(soon / they)
I hope!

14. Shana will be there _____later_____ .
(later / call)

15. Did you _____call_____ your
(call / soon)
dad yet?

16. He did _____great_____ on the test.
(soon / great)

17. When will _____they_____ be here?
(they / call)

Name _____

▶ High Frequency Words

A. Read each word. Then write it.

1. name   _____name_____

2. need   _____need_____

3. number   _____number_____

4. we   _____we_____

5. what   _____what_____

6. book   _____book_____

B. Write the missing letters.

7. Which word has 2 letters?

   __w__ __e__

8. Which words have 4 letters?

   __n__ __a__ __m__ __e__

   __n__ __e__ __e__ __d__

   __w__ __h__ __a__ __t__

   __b__ __o__ __o__ __k__

9. Which word has 6 letters?

   __n__ __u__ __m__ __b__ __e__ __r__

10. Which word ends with a **t**?

    __w__ __h__ __a__ __t__

11. Which word has an **r**?

    __n__ __u__ __m__ __b__ __e__ __r__

C. Write the missing word.

12. What is your _____name_____ ?
    (we / name)

13. Find the _____number_____ ten.
    (number / book)

14. The _____book_____ is on the shelf.
    (book / need)

15. _____We_____ went to the library.
    (We / Number)

16. I _____need_____ to do my
    (need / what)
    homework.

17. _____What_____ did you do last
    (What / We)
    week?

Name _____

► **High Frequency Words**

A. Read each word. Then write it.

1. boy _____ boy _____   4. group _____ group _____

2. day _____ day _____   5. letters _____ letters _____

3. girl _____ girl _____   6. night _____ night _____

7. year _____ year _____

B. Write the missing letters.

8. Which word ends with a **p**?

g   r   o   u   p
___ ___ ___ ___ ___

9. Which words have 3 letters?

b   o   y
___ ___ ___

d   a   y
___ ___ ___

10. Which words have 5 letters?

g   r   o   u   p
___ ___ ___ ___ ___

n   i   g   h   t
___ ___ ___ ___ ___

11. Which word ends with **s**?

l   e   t   t   e   r   s
___ ___ ___ ___ ___ ___ ___

12. Which words have a **y** in them?

y   e   a   r
___ ___ ___ ___

d   a   y
___ ___ ___

b   o   y
___ ___ ___

C. Write the missing word.

13. I saw the _____ boy _____ in class.
(night / boy)

14. Last _____ night _____, the sky
(group / night)
was clear.

15. He has many _____ letters _____
(letters / day)
from Tom.

16. During the _____ day _____ the sun
(day / night)
is out.

17. The _____ girl _____ plays basketball.
(year / girl)

18. There is a _____ group _____
(boy / group)
of students.

19. This _____ year _____ I am a freshman.
(night / year)

Name _____

► **Read on Your Own**

Read these sentences.

My quilt is big.

My rug is not big.

This ox is big.

This pup is not big.

That bus is very big!

That ant is not very big!

Foundations of Reading

Name _____

▶ Words with Short *a, i, o, e,* and *u*

A. Read each word. Draw a line to the correct picture.

1.
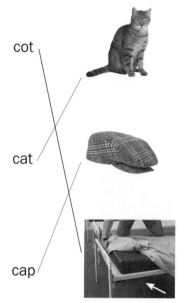

cot

cat

cap

2.
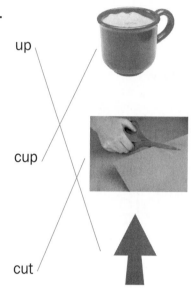

up

cup

cut

3.
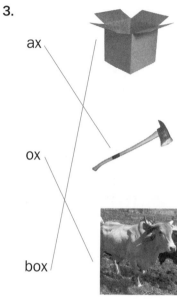

ax

ox

box

B. Say the name of each picture below. Write the missing letters.

4.

I can __z__ __i__ __p__ it.

6.

I like this old
__q__ __u__ __i__ __l__ __t__ .

8.

I have __s__ __i__ __x__
pins.

5.

This is my __b__ __u__ __s__ .

7.

Do you like my little
__p__ __u__ __p__ ?

9.

Is this a pig?
__Y__ __e__ __s__ !

F40

© NGSP & HB

Foundations of Reading

▶ Words with Short *a*, *i*, *o*, *e*, and *u*

A. Write the missing letters. Then read the words in each list. How are the words different?

1.
  _u_ _p_

  _c_ _u_ _p_

  _p_ _u_ _p_

2.
  _c_ _o_ _t_

  _c_ _a_ _t_

 _b_ _a_ _t_

3.
  _p_ _a_ _n_

  _p_ _e_ _n_

  _t_ _e_ _n_

B. Write the missing words.

4.

There is __m_ _i_ _l_ _k__
in my __c_ _u_ _p__ .

5.

Is this my __b_ _u_ _s__ ?

6.

He __c_ _u_ _t__ it.

7.

I have a
__q_ _u_ _i_ _l_ _t__.

8.

She can
__z_ _i_ _p__ it.

9.

Here is an
__a_ _n_ _t__ .

10.

There is a bug on my
__n_ _e_ _t__ .

11.

He has an __a_ _x__ .

12.

The lamp is not in the
__b_ _o_ _x__ .

Mind Map

Use the mind map to show what personal information is and how to share it. As you read the selections in this unit, add new ideas you learn about getting to know people.

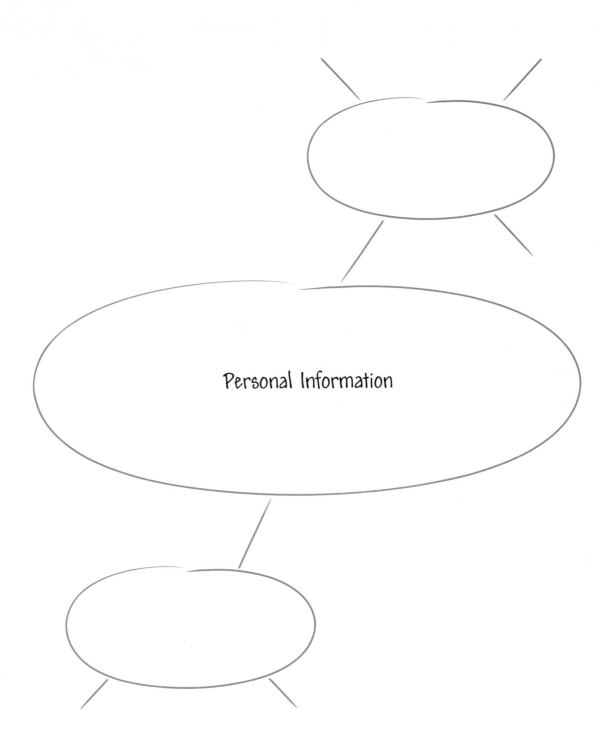

Personal Information

Use Pronouns in Greetings

▶ **Language: Exchange Greetings and Good-byes**

▶ **Grammar: Pronouns**

A. Study the chart.

Greetings and Good-byes

Greetings	Questions and Answers	Good-byes

Hi!	How are you?
	  I am fine.
	  We are fine, thank you.
		Bye!

Hello!		Good-bye!
Good morning!		So long!

Good afternoon!	How are you today?
	  I am okay.
	  We are well, thanks.
		Have a nice day!

Nice to meet you!		See you later!

B. Write what the people say. Use the chart.

Answers will vary. Sample responses are given.

1.

Good morning!

Hello!

Greetings

2.

How are you?

I am okay.

Question and Answer

3.

We are fine, thank you.

And how are you?

Question and Answer

4.

See you later!

Good-bye!

So long!

Good-byes

Name _____

Who Is It?

▶ **Grammar: Pronouns**

When you talk about other people or things, use the correct pronoun.

 For a girl or a woman, use **she.**

She is a student.

 For a boy or a man, use **he.**

He is a student, too.

 For a thing, use **it.**

It is a present.

 Use **they** to talk about more than one person or thing.

They are friends.

Complete each sentence. Add the correct pronoun.

1. Josef and Mikka sit together.

   ____They____ are friends.

2. Mikka is 13 years old today.

   ____She____ is a teenager now.

3. Josef has a present for Mikka.

   ____He____ is a good friend.

4. Mikka likes surprises.

   ____She____ takes the present.

5. The present makes Mikka smile.

   ____It____ is a CD by her favorite band.

6. The friends laugh.

   ____They____ are happy.

Language Development

Name _____

They Are in a Race

▶ **Grammar: Present Tense Verbs:** *Am, Is,* and *Are*

Use the verbs *am*, *is*, and *are* correctly.

Pronoun	Verb	Example
I	am	I **am** in P.E. class.
he she it	is	He **is** slow. She **is** in front of me. It **is** a nice day.
we you they	are	We **are** happy. You **are** fast! They **are** outside.

Complete each sentence. Add the correct verb.

1.

I ___am___ Lisa.

2.

She ___is___ in this race, too.

3.

He ___is___ behind us.

4.

I ___am___ not as fast as Jan.

5.

We say, "You ___are___ the winner, Jan!"

6.

Now we ___are___ ready to rest.

Name _____

How Can You Communicate?

▶ **Vocabulary: Communication**

▶ **Language: Use the Telephone**

A. Name each picture. Use words from the box.

| letter | fax | phone | e-mail |

1.

_____e-mail_____

2.

_____fax_____

3.

_____letter_____

4.

_____phone_____

B. You call Sam on the phone. Write what you say.

Answers will vary. Sample responses are given.

5. **You:** Hi, Sam. This is _____ .

   Sam: Hello. How are you?

6. **You:** I am fine, thanks. How can I order a school ___T-shirt/sweatshirt___ ?

   Sam: Send me an e-mail.

7. **You:** I do not have e-mail. Can I send you a ___fax/letter___ ?

   Sam: Sure. Tell the size and color you need.

8. **You:** Okay. Thanks for your help. ___Good-bye/Bye___ !

   Sam: You are welcome. See you tomorrow!

Language Development

Identify Sequence

▶ **Sum It Up**

A. Read about good news. Then make a sequence chain. Tell who gets the good news and how they get it. Tell about events in order.

> **Good News from Manuel**
>
> Marta gets a letter from Cousin Manuel. It is good news! Cousin Manuel is coming to visit!
>
> Marta sends an e-mail to her brother Rico to tell him the good news. Rico sends a fax to Grandfather to tell him the good news. Grandfather calls Uncle Ciro on the phone to tell him the good news. The good news travels fast!

Marta – letter

↓

Rico – e-mail

↓

Grandfather – fax

↓

Uncle Ciro – phone

B. Read each question. Write the answers.

1. What is the good news? _Cousin Manuel is coming to visit._

2. Who gets the news first? _Marta gets the news first._

3. Does Grandfather or Uncle Ciro get the news from Rico? _Grandfather_

4. Who gets the news last? _Uncle Ciro gets the news last._

Language and Literacy

High Frequency Words, Part 1

A. Read each word. Then write it.

1. from   _____from_____

2. home   _____home_____

3. new   _____new_____

4. go   _____go_____

5. there   _____there_____

B. Read each sentence. Find the new words in the box. Write the words on the lines.

6. These two words have an **m**.

    _____from_____   _____home_____

7. This word has 3 letters.

    _____new_____

8. This word is the opposite of **stop**.

    _____go_____

9. This word rhymes with **where**.

    _____there_____

10. This word starts with **fr**.

    _____from_____

High Frequency Words, Part 2

A. Read each word. Then write it.

1. many	_____many_____
2. first	_____first_____
3. next	_____next_____
4. then	_____then_____
5. one	_____one_____

B. Read each sentence. Find the new words in the box. Write the words on the lines.

6. This word has an **m**.

_____many_____

7. These 3 words tell "when."

_____first_____   _____next_____   _____then_____

8. This word has 3 letters.

_____one_____

9. These 3 words have 4 letters each.

_____many_____   _____next_____   _____then_____

10. This word has an **o**.

_____one_____

Words with Short *a* and Short *o*

A. Name each picture. Write the name.

1.

clock

2.

cot

3.

pot

4.

cat

5.

van

6.

hat

7.

mop

8.

pan

B. Now read the story. Circle the words with short *a* or short *o*. Write them in the chart. Write each word one time.

Cat Fun

Sam has a cat.

The cat has lots of fun.

It hops on the hat.

It naps in a pot.

It got into a pan.

It sleeps on the van.

When the cat is hot,

It jumps on the cot.

The cat can be bad.

But Sam likes his cat!

9. cat	18. lots
10. Sam	19. hops
11. has	20. on
12. hat	21. pot
13. naps	22. got
14. pan	23. hot
15. van	24. cot
16. can	
17. bad	

Name _____

Words with Short *a* and Short *o*

A. Name each picture. Write the name.

1.

hat

2.

pot

3.

fan

4.

mop

5.

cot

6.

map

7.

tag

8.
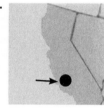
dot

B. Now read the story. Circle the words with short *a* or short *o*. Write them in the chart. Write each word one time.

I See a (Van)

I see a (van).

It (has) a (lot) of things in it!

I see a (map) and a (box) in the (van).

I see a (mop) and a (fan) in the (van).

I see some (pots) and (pans), too.

Is (Tom) in the (van)?

(Tom) is (not) in the (van). There is no room!

9. van	15. lot
10. has	16. box
11. map	17. mop
12. and	18. pots
13. fan	19. Tom
14. pans	20. not

Words with Short *a* and Short *o*

A. Read each word. Which picture goes with the word? Write its letter.

1. fan _B_   2. box _C_   3. cap _O_   4. flag _D_   5. apple _G_

6. dot _H_   7. rock _E_   8. bat _K_   9. jog _F_   10. tag _L_

11. map _I_   12. spots _A_   13. ox _M_   14. cloth _J_   15. frog _N_

A.    B.    C.    D.    E.

F.   G.    H. 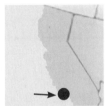   I.    J.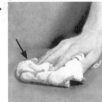

K.   L.    M.    N.    O.

B. Name each picture below. Which word or words above rhyme with the picture name? Write the words on the lines.

16.   flag   tag

17.   jog   frog

18.   bat

Words with Short *a* and Short *o*

A. Read each word. Which picture goes with the word? Write its letter.

1. cot ___G___	2. cap ___E___	3. fan ___J___	4. top ___K___	5. jog ___O___
6. bag ___B___	7. fog ___C___	8. dot ___H___	9. van ___A___	10. rag ___F___
11. hop ___L___	12. bat ___N___	13. nap ___I___	14. hat ___M___	15. sad ___D___

A.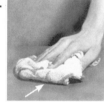

B.

C.

D.

E.

F.

G.

H.

I.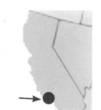

J.

K.

L.

M.

N.

O.

B. Read each word. Find the word or words above that have the same vowel sound and spelling. Write the words on the lines.

16. cap / nap

17. bag / rag

18. hop / top

19. bat / hat

20.  fan / van

21. cot / dot

22. jog

23. sad

Build Reading Fluency

▶ Expression

A. Some sentences tell something. Other sentences show strong feeling.

This sentence tells something.
It ends with a period.

    Lupe is new at Lakeside School .

This sentence shows a strong feeling.
It ends with an exclamation mark.

    Lupe is glad to have 2 new friends !

B. Listen to the different kinds of sentences.

> **New at School**
>
> Lupe is new at Lakeside School.
> First she has science lab with Pat and Ron.
> Pat helps Lupe.
> They have many things to do.
> Next they have P.E. class.
> They go from one class to the next.
> Pat and Lupe go fast. Ron does not go fast.
> He has a cold and has to stop!
> Then Pat, Lupe, and Ron go to lunch.
> They have a lot of hot soup there.
> At last it is time to go home.
> Lupe is glad to have 2 new friends!

C. Now read the sentences above. Work with a partner. Say each kind of sentence with the right expression. See how your reading improves!

Everything Is New!

▶ Statements and Exclamations

A. Some sentences tell something. Other sentences show a strong feeling.

This sentence tells something. It ends with a period.

Vu has a new jacket **.**

All sentences start with a capital letter.

She goes to a new school today.

This sentence shows a strong feeling. It ends with an exclamation mark.

She loves it **!**

B. Complete each sentence. Start each sentence with a capital letter. Add a period or an exclamation mark at the end.

1. __Vu__ opens her new locker.
   (Vu)

2. It is very small __!__

3. She puts her jacket in it __.__

4. Vu meets her new teacher __.__

5. __He__ teaches English.
   (he)

6. He is very tall __!__

7. Vu walks home __.__

8. __She__ sees snow for the first time.
   (she)

9. She loves the snow __!__

10. This is a great day __!__

Learn Key Vocabulary

Name _____

Many People to Meet: Key Vocabulary

A. Study each word. Circle a number to rate how well you know it. Then complete the chart.

Rating Scale	**1** I have never seen this word before.	**2** I am not sure of the word's meaning.	**3** I know this word and can teach the word's meaning to someone else.

▲ There are many **people** to **meet** in your neighborhood.

Key Words	Check Understanding	Deepen Understanding
❶ first (furst) *adverb* Rating: 1 2 3	If you are **first**, you are at the end of the line. Yes (No)	What is the first thing you say when you see a friend? *Responses will vary but may include the words* hi, hello, *and* what's up?
❷ home (hōm) *noun* Rating: 1 2 3	A **home** can be a house or apartment. (Yes) No	Describe your home. *Responses will vary. Possible responses could relate to what the home looks like or where it is located.*
❸ meet (mēt) *verb* Rating: 1 2 3	When you **meet** a friend for lunch, you sit together and talk while you eat. (Yes) No	Where do you meet friends? *Responses will vary but should relate to a meeting place.*

Name _____

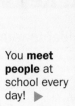 You **meet people** at school every day! ▶

Key Words	Check Understanding	Deepen Understanding
❹ next (nekst) *adverb* **Rating:** 1 2 3	I mail a letter. I put a stamp on it **next**. Yes (No)	Suppose you are next. How many people are in front of you? *Students should respond that just one person would be in front of them.* _____ _____ _____
❺ people (pē-pul) *noun* **Rating:** 1 2 3	Boys and girls are **people**. (Yes) No	Name three people in your class. *Responses will vary but should mention the names of three real classmates.* _____ _____ _____

B. Use at least two of the Key Vocabulary words. Tell about a day when you met someone for the first time.   *Answers will vary.*

_____

_____

_____

Name _____

Plan and Write

1. Who will you write to? What do you want to say? Make a list of names and possible topics.

Names	Topics
_____	_____
_____	_____
_____	_____

2. Choose a focus. Circle one name and topic.

Turn your ideas into sentences. Write your e-mail.

3. Fill in your friend's name after To:

4. Fill in your name after From:

5. Fill in the date after Sent:

6. Fill in the topic after Subject:

7. Write a greeting.

8. Write your message. Share your news.

9. Write a closing like *Love*, *See you soon*, or *Your friend*. Use a comma after the closing.

10. Write your name.

To: _____

From: _____

Sent: _____

Subject: _____

Hi _____,

How are you? I am _____. I have news for you.

I _____

_____

_____

_____

_____

Check Your Work

▶ Capitalization and End Marks

Read the e-mail. Fix capital letters and end punctuation as needed.
Mark your changes. Then write the sentences correctly.

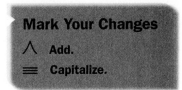

Mark Your Changes

∧ Add.

≡ Capitalize.

To: robert@teenschool.com

From: Luis

Sent: October 5, 2008

Subject: My soccer team

Hi Robert,

How are you? I am great I joined a soccer team at school. We are called the Wildcats. We

practice three times a week We had our first game last Wednesday. our team won 2 to 1.

I scored one point! I wish you were on my team write back soon.

Your friend,

Luis

_____ Hi Robert,

_____ How are you? I am great! I joined a soccer team at school. We are called the Wildcats. We practice three times

_____ a week. We had our first game last Wednesday. Our team won 2 to 1. I scored one point! I wish you were on my

_____ team. Write back soon.

_____ Your friend,

_____ Luis

_____

_____

_____

_____

_____

_____

Unit 2 Launch

Mind Map

Use the mind map to show what you know about food. As you read the selections in this unit, add new ideas you learn about different types of food.

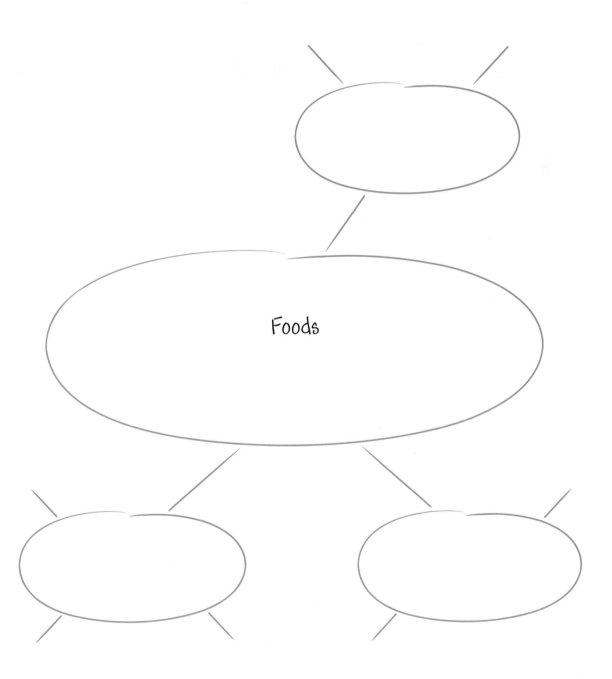

Lunch Looks Good!

▶ **Vocabulary: Colors, Shapes, and Sizes**

▶ **Language: Describe**

A. Look at each picture. Tell the size or shape. Use a word from the box.

Answers will vary. Sample responses are given.

| small | round | square | long | triangular | rectangular |

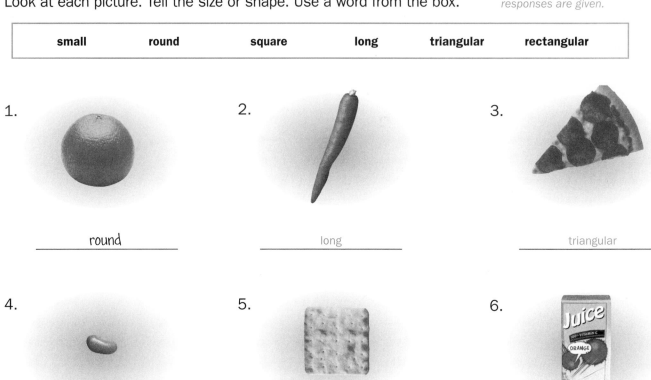

1.
round

2.
long

3.
triangular

4.
small

5.
square

6.
rectangular

B. Complete the sentences. Add words to tell the color, size, or shape.

Answers will vary. Sample responses are given.

7. I eat pizza with my friends. We sit at a _____rectangular_____ table.

8. The pizza box has four equal sides. The box is _____square_____ .

9. We do not eat a small pizza. We eat a _____large_____ pizza.

10. The pizza is like a circle. It is _____round_____ .

11. There is cheese on our pizza. The color is _____yellow_____ , like a banana.

12. My slice of pizza is like a triangle. It is _____triangular_____ .

What's for Lunch?

▶ **Vocabulary: Foods**

▶ **Language: Describe**

A. Name each food. Use words from the box.

butter	chicken	milk	plum	pear	peas	roll	water

pear

milk

peas

butter

plum

water

chicken

roll

B. Complete each sentence. Tell about the food. Then name it.

Answers will vary. Sample responses are given.

1.

This is a kind of bread. You can put ____butter____ on it. It is a ____roll____ .

2.

This is a cold drink. It is in a tall ____glass____ . It is ____water____ .

3.
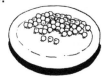
These are green. They are ____small____ in size. They are ____peas____ .

4.

This is a fruit. It has a ____round____ shape. It is a ____plum____ .

Let's Eat Salad

▶ **Grammar: Action Verbs**

An action verb tells what someone does.

I **make** tasty salads.

I **find** fresh lettuce.

I **take** a red tomato.

I **get** some carrots, too.

Action Verbs

wash	cut	eat	add	put	get

Complete each sentence. Tell how to make a salad. Use verbs from the box.

1.

I _____wash_____ the lettuce.

2.

I _____get_____ some carrots.

3.

I _____cut_____ the tomato.

4.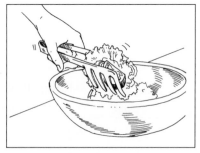

I _____put_____ the salad in a bowl.

5.

I _____add_____ the dressing.

6.

I _____eat_____ the salad!

Identify Steps in a Process

▶ **Sum It Up**

A. Think about how to make a hamburger. Put the steps in order.

___5___ Put the burger on a bun.

___3___ Shape the meat into a round burger.

___4___ Cook the burger.

___1___ Put meat, onions, egg, salt, and pepper in a bowl.

___2___ Mix the ingredients together.

B. Use the steps to make a sequence chain. Tell about how to make a hamburger.

Put meat, onions, egg, salt, and pepper in a bowl.

↓

Mix all the ingredients together.

↓

Shape the meat into a round burger.

↓

Cook the burger.

↓

Put the burger on a bun.

High Frequency Words, Part 1

A. Read each word. Then write it.

1. something _____ something _____

2. make _____ make _____

3. long _____ long _____

4. large _____ large _____

5. move _____ move _____

B. Read the clue. Write the word in the chart. Then write the word again in the sentence.

What to Look For	Word	Sentence
6. has the word **some** in it	s o m e t h i n g	I want _____ something _____ hot.
7. rhymes with **take**	m a k e	You _____ make _____ great food.
8. rhymes with **song**	l o n g	I like _____ long _____ noodles.
9. means "big"	l a r g e	You have a _____ large _____ bag.
10. ends with **ve**	m o v e	Please _____ move _____ over.

Name _____

High Frequency Words, Part 2

A. Read each word. Then write it.

1. different _____different_____

2. small _____small_____

3. open _____open_____

4. same _____same_____

5. eat _____eat_____

B. Read the clue. Write the word in the chart. Then write the word again in the sentence.

What to Look For	Word	Sentence
6. has **ff**	d i f f e r e n t	Your bag is ___different___ .
7. starts with **sm**	s m a l l	My lunch is in a ___small___ bag.
8. starts with **o**	o p e n	I ___open___ my lunch bag.
9. ends with **me**	s a m e	Our food is not the ___same___ .
10. has three letters	e a t	It is time to ___eat___ .

Name _____

Words with Short *i* and Short *u*

A. Name each picture. Write the name.

1.

   __pig__

2.

   cup

3.

   pup

4.

   wig

5.

   fish

6.

   sun

7.

   six

8.

   rug

B. Now read the story. Circle the words with short *i* or short *u*. Write them in the chart. Write each word one time.

My New (Pup)

Yesterday I got a new (pup).
She (sips)(milk) from a (little)(cup).
We (sit)(in) the (sun).
Then we go for a (run).
I know one day my (pup)(will) get (big).
I hope she never looks like a (pig)!
For now I (just) love my (silly)(mutt).

9. sips	15. pup
10. little	16. cup
11. sit	17. sun
12. big	18. run
13. pig	19. just
14. silly	20. mutt
	21. milk
	22. will
	23. in

Language and Literacy

Words with Short *i* and Short *u*

A. Name each picture. Write the name.

1.

_____pin_____

2.

_____run_____

3.

_____pig_____

4.

_____jump_____

5.

_____nut_____

6.

_____cup_____

7.

_____lid_____

8.

_____disk_____

B. Now read the story. Circle the words with short *i* or short *u*. Write them in the chart. Write each word one time.

⟨Just⟩ Great!

Sam needs something to eat.
He ⟨rips⟩ open a bag of ⟨chips⟩.
The ⟨chips⟩ are good, ⟨but⟩ not great.
Sam ⟨cuts⟩ a ⟨bit⟩ of ham and
slaps ⟨it⟩ on a ⟨bun⟩.
The ham ⟨is⟩ good, ⟨but⟩ not great.
Mom comes ⟨in⟩.
She gets a ⟨cup⟩ of ice cream.
She adds lots of ⟨nuts⟩.
Sam ⟨grins⟩. Yes! That ⟨is⟩ great!

9. _____Just_____	15. _____rips_____
10. _____but_____	16. _____chips_____
11. _____cuts_____	17. _____bit_____
12. _____bun_____	18. _____it_____
13. _____cup_____	19. _____is_____
14. _____nuts_____	20. _____in_____
	21. _____grins_____

Words with Short *i* and Short *u*

A. Read each word. Which picture goes with the word? Write its letter.

1. cup   G
2. fin   D
3. pump   L
4. hit   F
5. sit   A
6. rug   B
7. disk   M
8. nut   J
9. pig   K
10. dig   N
11. sun   H
12. pin   I
13. cut   C
14. lid   O
15. bun   E

A.
B.
C.
D.
E.

F.
G.
H.
I.
J.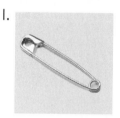

K.
L.
M.
N.
O.

B. Name each picture below. Which word or words above rhyme with the picture name? Write the words on the lines.

16.   bun / sun

17.   pump

18.   pig / dig

19.   rug

20.   cup

21.   sit / fit

22.   fin / pin

Name _____

Words with Short *i* and Short *u*

A. Write the missing letters. Then read the words in each list. How are the words different?

1.

<u>p</u> <u>i</u> <u>n</u>

<u>h</u> <u>i</u> <u>t</u>

<u>s</u> <u>i</u> <u>t</u>

2.

<u>b</u> <u>u</u> <u>s</u>

<u>u</u> <u>p</u>

<u>c</u> <u>u</u> <u>t</u>

B. Read each question. What word goes in the answer? Spell the word. Then circle the correct picture.

3. Where is the cup? The <u>c</u> <u>u</u> <u>p</u> is here.

6. Where is the pup? The <u>p</u> <u>u</u> <u>p</u> is here.

4. Who made a hit? John made a <u>h</u> <u>i</u> <u>t</u>.

7. Who can zip it? The girl can <u>z</u> <u>i</u> <u>p</u> it.

5. Where is the first-aid kit? The first-aid <u>k</u> <u>i</u> <u>t</u> is here.

8. Where is the fish? Here is the <u>f</u> <u>i</u> <u>s</u> <u>h</u>.

Build Reading Fluency

▶ **Phrasing**

A. When you read, pause between groups of words that go together.

Kim likes hot dogs / for lunch.
She cooks / a batch of hot dogs / in a big pot.

B. Listen to the story. Which groups of words does the reader say together? Where does he pause? When you hear a pause, write a /.

Example: Kim likes hot dogs / for lunch.

Something Good for Lunch

Kim likes hot dogs/for lunch.
She cooks/a batch of hot dogs/in a big pot.
Next/Kim chops some small onions.
She opens/a large bag of buns.
She fills the buns with hot dogs,/mustard,/and onions.
She opens/a bag of chips/too.
She pours/a cup of punch.
This is too much food to eat!
Kim calls Mitch.
Then they sit and eat/a great lunch!/

B. Now read the story to a partner. Read groups of words together. Pause when you see a /.

I Am Not a Cook!

► **Negative Sentences**

A. A negative sentence has a negative word, like *not*.

The fish is **not** big.
The carrots are **not** long.
Meg is **not** happy.

B. Look at each picture. Complete the sentence.
Add a verb and the word *not*.

1.

I _____am_____ _____not_____ a
good cook.

2.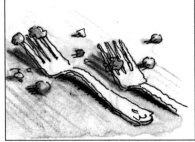

The forks _____are_____ _____not_____
clean.

3.

The plates _____are_____
_____not_____ on the table.

4.

The pasta _____is_____ _____not_____
in the water.

5.

The rolls _____are_____ _____not_____
hot.

6.

Dinner _____is_____ _____not_____
ready!

Name _____

U.S. Tour of Food: Key Vocabulary

A. Study each word. Circle a number to rate how well you know it.
Then complete the chart.

Rating Scale	**1** I have never seen this word before.	**2** I am not sure of the word's meaning.	**3** I know this word and can teach the word's meaning to someone else.

▲ Fruit comes in different **colors, shapes,** and **sizes.**

Key Words	Check Understanding	Deepen Understanding
❶ color (kuh-ler) *noun* **Rating:** 1 2 3	Purple is a dark **color.** (Yes) No	What color do you like best? *Responses will vary but should name a color.*
❷ foods (fūdz) *noun* **Rating:** 1 2 3	Paper and pens are **foods.** Yes (No)	Name two foods that you like a lot. *Responses will vary but should name two foods.*
❸ shapes (shāps) *noun* **Rating:** 1 2 3	Apples and oranges have round **shapes.** (Yes) No	Name some shapes. *Responses will vary but should name some shapes.*

Name _____

There are
many kinds
of **foods** at
a farmers'
market. ▶

Key Words	Check Understanding	Deepen Understanding
❹ sizes (sizez) *noun* **Rating: 1 2 3**	Grapes and shrimp have small **sizes**. (Yes) No	What are some sizes of nuts? *Responses will vary but should name reasonable sizes for nuts.*
❺ visit (**vi**-zit) *verb* **Rating: 1 2 3**	Friends may **visit** each other. (Yes) No	What people do you visit? *Responses will vary but should relate to people students might visit.*

B. Use at least two of the Key Vocabulary words. Describe foods you ate at
your last meal.

Answers will vary.

_____

_____

_____

Name _____

Plan and Write

1. What art can you make with food? Make a list. Draw pictures of what the food will look like.

Food: _____	Food: _____	Food: _____

2. Choose one idea for your How-To Card. Put a check mark next to the one you choose.

3. Think about the food you need. Plan each step. Write each step.

1.	→	2.	→	3.	→	4.

4. Fill in the title.

5. Write the steps. Use adjectives and action verbs.

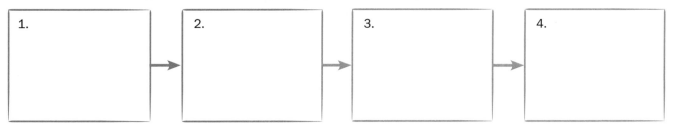

How to Make _____

1. I get _____

2. I _____

3. I _____

4. I _____

5. I _____

Check Your Work

▶ Capitalization and Adding Words

Read the How-To Card. Fix capital letters. Add an action verb if one is missing from a step. Add adjectives to tell color, shape, or how many. Mark your changes.

How to Make a Rabbit Face

1. i put a pear half on a plate.

2. then I add peach slices for ears.

   add
3. I coconut for the rabbit's fur.

   two
4. I put raisins for eyes.

   red
5. last, I add a cherry for the nose.

Draw a picture of what the finished rabbit face might look like.

Name _____

Mind Map

Use the mind map to show workers at school, their jobs, and the tools they use to do their jobs. As you read the selections in this unit, add new ideas you learn about the work that people do.

Worker	Job	Tools

Tell About the Jobs They Do

► **Language: Give Information**
► **Vocabulary: Actions and Careers**

A. Study the charts.

Careers	Actions
artist	draw
cab driver	drive
carpenter	build

Careers	Actions
gardener	plant
police officer	protect
teacher	teach

B. Complete each sentence. Use the chart.

1.

He is an ___artist___ .

He can ___draw___ and paint.

2.

She is a ___carpenter___ .

She can ___build___ things.

3.

Here is a ___gardener___ .

She can ___plant___ flowers.

4.

She can ___protect___ us.

She is a ___police officer___ .

5.

He is a ___teacher___ .

He can ___teach___ us how to write.

6.

This is a ___cab driver___ .

He can ___drive___ people places.

Language Development

Everyone Helps

▶ Grammar: Present Tense Verbs

To tell what another person or thing does, use a verb that ends in **-s**.

The Ali family **owns** a store.

It **keeps** them busy.

Mr. Ali **works** hard.

Mrs. Ali **helps**.

Read each sentence. Add the correct form of the action verb.

1.

Mr. Ali _____cleans_____ .
       (clean)

He _____sweeps_____ the sidewalk.
    (sweep)

2.

He _____moves_____ a box for Mr. Ali.
    (move)

It _____holds_____ fresh apples.
    (hold)

3.

Mrs. Ali _____takes_____ the money.
       (take)

She _____thanks_____ the man.
    (thank)

4.

Kira _____cuts_____ a flower.
    (cut)

She _____puts_____ it in water.
    (put)

Name _____

What Tools Do They Use?

▶ **Vocabulary: Tools and Careers**

▶ **Language: Ask and Answer Questions**

A. Name the tool each worker has. Use words from the box.

brush	pencil	notebook	wrench	paper	computer	scissors

Artist

paper

pencil

Stylist

scissors

brush

Mechanic

wrench

Writer

computer

notebook

B. Look at the pictures above. Read each question. Write the answer.

1. Can the artist draw?

   Yes, she can.

2. Is the writer in an office?

   Yes, she is.

3. Are the stylist and the boy in a garage?

   No, they are not.

4. Is the notebook open?

   Yes, it is.

5. Can the mechanic use a wrench?

   Yes, he can.

6. Is the wrench on the floor?

   No, it is not.

Identify Details

▶ **Sum It Up**

A. Read about Hana's morning. Then make a concept web to show the people who help her.

> **Hana's Helpers**
>
> Hana is in a hurry to get to class. She leaves her library book on the bus. The bus driver finds the book. He gives it to the custodian. The custodian takes the book to the school office. An office worker takes the book to Hana's teacher.
>
> Hana's teacher gives the book back to Hana. Hana is happy to get the book! That afternoon, Hana takes the book to the library. The librarian helps Hana renew the book so she can finish reading it.

B. Finish the paragraph. Use details from your concept web.

Hana wants to thank everyone who helped her. She starts by thanking the

_____librarian_____ who helps her renew the book. Then Hana goes to the classroom

and thanks her _____teacher_____ . As Hana gets on the bus to go home, she thanks

the _____bus driver_____ . The next morning, Hana thanks the _____custodian_____

and the _____office worker_____ at school.

High Frequency Words, Part 1

A. Read each word. Then write it.

1. study   _____study_____

2. learn   _____learn_____

3. carry   _____carry_____

4. find   _____find_____

5. use   _____use_____

B. Read each sentence. Find the new words in the box. Write the words on the lines.

6. This word starts with **st**.

_____study_____

7. This word starts with **l**.

_____learn_____

8. These 3 words have 5 letters each.

_____carry_____   _____learn_____   _____study_____

9. This word has an **i**.

_____find_____

10. This word ends with **e**.

_____use_____

High Frequency Words, Part 2

A. Read each word. Then write it.

1. love   _____love_____

2. face   _____face_____

3. when   _____when_____

4. want   _____want_____

5. say   _____say_____

B. Read each sentence. Find the new words in the box. Write the words on the lines.

6. This word starts with **l**.

_____love_____

7. These 2 words end with **e**.

_____face_____   _____love_____

8. This word rhymes with **then**.

_____when_____

9. This word ends with **nt**.

_____want_____

10. This word rhymes with **day**.

_____say_____

Words with Short e

A. Read each word. Which picture goes with the word? Write its letter.

1. web _G_   2. fence _C_   3. bell _F_

4. desk _D_   5. ten _H_   6. hen _E_

7. egg _A_   8. vest _B_   9. leg _I_

A.

B.

C.

D.

E.

F.

G.

H.

I.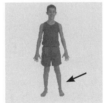

B. Read each sentence. Write the correct word on the line.

10. This word rhymes with **best**.

_____vest_____

11. This word rhymes with **tell**.

_____bell_____

Words with Short e

A. Read each word. Which picture goes with the word? Write its letter.

1. hen _F_   2. check _E_   3. net _C_   4. pet _A_

5. bed _B_   6. chest _H_   7. pen _D_   8. vet _G_

9. egg _K_   10. bench _L_   11. stretch _I_   12. send _J_

A.

B.

C.

D.

E.

F.

G.

H.

I.

J.

K.

L.

B. Name each picture below. Which words above rhyme with the picture name? Write the words on the lines.

13.    _pet_

    net

    vet

14.    _pen_

    hen

Name _____

Final *ll, ss, zz, ck*

A. Read each word. Which picture goes with the word? Write its letter.

1. chick __A__   2. pill __B__   3. bell __H__   4. fizz __F__

5. check __C__   6. jazz __I__   7. kiss __G__   8. spill __D__

9. rock __E__   10. sick __J__   11. dress __L__   12. hill __K__

A.

B.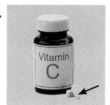

C.

D.

E.

F.

G.

H.

I.

J.

K.

L.

B. Name each picture below. What is the last sound? Find the words above that have the same sound at the end. Write the words on the lines.

13.    pill

bell

spill

hill

14.    chick

check

rock

sick

Words with *sh*

A. Read each word. Which picture goes with the word? Write its letter.

1. shirt __B__   2. fish ___F___   3. trash ___E___

4. ship __D__   5. shell ___C___   6. shoulder ___A___

A.

B.

C.

D.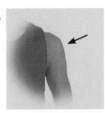

E.

F.

B. Now read the story. Circle the words with the *sh* sound. Write the words in the chart. Write each word one time.

Shiny New Shoes

I have a pair of shiny new shoes. They are a pale shade of blue. I think the shoelaces are too short. After school, I will take them back to the shop. I will show the laces to the salesman. I will not be shy. Tonight I will put my new shoes on a shelf. I will shut the door and go to sleep.

7.	shiny	12.	shop
8.	shoes	13.	show
9.	shade	14.	shy
10.	shoelaces	15.	shelf
11.	short	16.	shut

Build Reading Fluency

▶ Intonation

A. Some sentences ask something. Other sentences show strong feeling.

This sentence asks a question.
It ends with a question mark.

> Do you want to send something **?**

This sentence shows a strong feeling.
It ends with an exclamation mark.

> Then he hops on his bike and … zip **!**

B. Listen to the reader's voice. Listen for sentences that ask
a question or show a strong feeling.

> ### Let Ben Take It
>
> Ben is a bike messenger.
> Do you want to send something?
> Ben can get it there fast.
> Just say where it must go.
> He gets his map.
> He can study it to learn the best route.
> He uses it to find a shop.
> Then he hops on his bike and … zip!
> He is off like a jet.
> Ben can carry a lot of different things:
> food, pictures, letters, flowers.
> They fit in the big bag on his back.
> Ben loves his job.
> He has a smile on his face.
> When you want to send something,
> let Ben take it!

C. Now read the sentences to a partner. See how your reading improves!

Name _____

Who? What? Where? When?

▶ **Questions with** *Who, What, Where,* **and** *When*

A. You can use the words *Who, What, Where,* or *When* to start a question.

Use *Who* to ask about a person.

   Who is this?

Use *What* to ask about a thing.

   What is his job?

Use *Where* to ask about a place.

   Where can he go?

Use *When* to ask about a time.

   When is he at work?

B. Complete each question. Use *Who, What, Where,* or *When.*

1. ___Who___ drives the cab?
   Mr. Siwela drives the cab.

2. ___What___ is on his head?
   A cap is on his head.

3. ___Where___ is the cab?
   The cab is at the flower shop.

4. ___Where___ is the shop?
   The shop is on Main Street.

5. ___Who___ wants a ride in the cab?
   Ms. Vega wants a ride.

6. ___What___ is in her hand?
   A plant is in her hand.

7. ___When___ is she ready to go?
   She is ready to go now.

8. ___Where___ is her home?
   Her home is on Elm Street.

Learn Key Vocabulary

Name _____

Geologists–Rock Scientists: Key Vocabulary

A. Study each word. Circle a number to rate how well you know it. Then complete the chart.

Rating Scale	**1** I have never seen this word before.	**2** I am not sure of the word's meaning.	**3** I know this word and can teach the word's meaning to someone else.

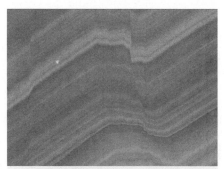

▲ **Scientists** called geologists can tell how old this **rock** is by **studying** its layers.

Key Words	Check Understanding	Deepen Understanding
❶ **learn** (lurn) *verb* Rating: 1 2 3	To become a doctor, you must **learn** about the human body. (Yes) No	What do you like to learn about? *Responses will vary but should name areas of study.*
❷ **rock** (rok) *noun* Rating: 1 2 3	Most kinds of **rock** are soft. Yes (No)	Describe a kind of rock in your area. *Responses will vary but should include descriptions of rocks.*
❸ **scientist** (sī-yun-tist) *noun* Rating: 1 2 3	A **scientist** studies nature. (Yes) No	Name a kind of scientist. *Responses will vary. Possible responses include geologists, chemists, biologists, and physicists.*

Name _____

Scientists use tools to find clues in **rocks** about the past. ▶

Key Words	Check Understanding	Deepen Understanding
4 study (stuh-dē) *verb* Rating:　1　2　3	When you **study** science, you learn about plants and animals. (Yes)　　　No	What will you study today? *Responses will vary but should name subject areas students are likely to study today.* _____ _____ _____
5 use (yūz) *verb* Rating:　1　2　3	Chefs **use** pots and pans. (Yes)　　　No	What tools do farmers use? *Responses will vary but should relate to tools used in planting and growing.* _____ _____ _____

B. Use at least two of the Key Vocabulary words. Imagine you are a geologist. What would your day be like?

Answers will vary.

_____

_____

_____

Plan and Write

1. What worker will you interview? Name the worker's job. _____

2. What do you want to know? Make a list.

   _____   _____

   _____   _____

   _____   _____

3. Choose a focus. Check three items.

4. Turn your ideas into questions. Write the questions. End each question with a
   question mark. Leave room for answers.

   Q: What is _____

   A: My name is _____

   _____

   Q: Where do _____

   A: I work _____

   _____

   Q: What is _____

   A: _____

   _____

   Q: What do you like _____

   A: I like _____

   _____

   Q: _____

   A: _____

   _____

5. Study the questions. Interview a worker. Write your answers and get a photo or
   draw a picture of the person.

Check Your Work

▶ Capitalization and End Marks

Read the interview. Fix capital letters and end marks where they are needed. Mark your changes. Then write the sentences correctly.

Animal Doctor

Q: what is your name and what is your job?

_____What is your name and what is your job?_____

A: my name is Martin Lee and I am an animal doctor.

_____My name is Martin Lee and I am an animal doctor._____

Q: where do you work?

_____Where do you work?_____

A: i work in an animal hospital on Park Street.

_____I work in an animal hospital on Park Street._____

Q: what made you want to do this job?

_____What made you want to do this job?_____

A: i have always loved animals i lived on a farm when I was growing up.

_____I have always loved animals. I lived on a farm when I was growing up._____

_____

Q: what do you like best about your job?

_____What do you like best about your job?_____

A: my favorite thing is seeing animals get better my work makes people happy,

too that's because pets are very important to people.

_____My favorite thing is seeing animals get better. My work makes people happy, too. That's because pets are_____

_____very important to people._____

_____

Name _____

Mind Map

Use the mind map to show the different things that numbers can tell you. As you read the selections in this unit, add new ideas you learn about how numbers are used.

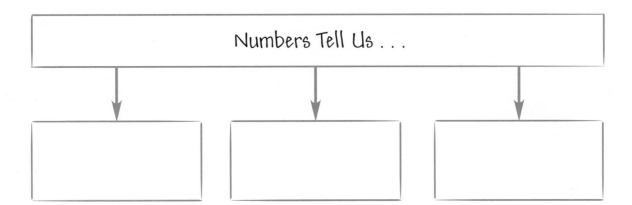

Numbers Tell Us . . .

What Questions Do They Ask?

▶ **Language: Ask Questions**

▶ **Grammar: Questions with *Do* and *Does***

Complete each question. Then complete the answer.
Use *do* or *does*.

1.

2.

3.

4.

Language Development

Name _____

Numbers Tell How Many

▶ **Vocabulary: Cardinal Numbers**

▶ **Language: Give Information**

A. Read the number words. Write the numbers.

1. four thousand, five hundred forty ⎯⎯⎯ 4,540 ⎯⎯⎯

2. nine hundred ninety-seven ⎯⎯⎯ 997 ⎯⎯⎯

3. three hundred ten thousand ⎯⎯⎯ 310,000 ⎯⎯⎯

4. two million, one hundred thousand ⎯⎯⎯ 2,100,000 ⎯⎯⎯

5. fifty-four thousand, one hundred one ⎯⎯⎯ 54,101 ⎯⎯⎯

6. eight hundred thirty-eight ⎯⎯⎯ 838 ⎯⎯⎯

7. five thousand, six hundred fourteen ⎯⎯⎯ 5,614 ⎯⎯⎯

8. seven hundred nineteen ⎯⎯⎯ 719 ⎯⎯⎯

9. thirty million, two hundred thousand ⎯⎯⎯ 30,200,000 ⎯⎯⎯

10. ten thousand, four hundred one ⎯⎯⎯ 10,401 ⎯⎯⎯

B. Complete the facts about this student's school. Use number words.

11. My school __has three fields__ .
       (3 fields)

12. My school __has twelve classrooms__ .
       (12 classrooms)

13. My school __has twenty-four computers__ .
       (24 computers)

    _____ .

14. My school __has three hundred forty-seven students__
       (347 students)

    _____ .

I Am Not Ready!

▶ Grammar: Negative Sentences

There are different ways to build negative sentences.

Add **not** after **am, is,** or **are**.

He is ready.   He is not ready.

Add **do not** or **does not** before other verbs.

He gets on the bus.   He does not get on the bus.

A. Make each sentence a negative sentence. Use a verb and the word *not*.

1. I am ready for the game.

   I _____am not_____ ready for the game.

2. The bus is on time.

   The bus _____is not_____ on time.

3. We are on Bus 5.

   We _____are not_____ on Bus 5.

B. Make each sentence a negative sentence. Add *do not* or *does not*.

4. The bus driver leaves at 4:00.

   The bus driver _____does not leave_____ at 4:00.

5. She closes the doors.

   She _____does not close_____ the doors.

6. The players go to the game.

   The players _____do not go_____ to the game.

First, Second, Third . . .

▶ **Vocabulary: Ordinal Numbers**

▶ **Language: Express Needs**

A. Look at the picture. In what order are the people?
Write words from the box to show the order.

first	second	third	fourth	fifth	sixth	seventh	eighth	ninth	tenth

My bag does not have a tag.

I am hungry!

B. Use the picture above to complete each sentence. Tell what the person needs.

mother	sneakers	bag	food	tag

1. The first person needs _____sneakers_____ .

2. The fourth person needs a _____tag_____ .

3. The sixth person needs a big _____bag_____ .

4. The seventh person needs his _____mother_____ .

5. The tenth person needs _____food_____ .

Identify Problem and Solution

▶ **Sum It Up**

Read the story. Complete the problem-and-solution chart. Use your chart to retell the story to a partner.

> ### Friends to the Rescue
>
> Morris opened his lunch bag as he talked to his friends. Suddenly, his face changed. He pulled out two small toy trucks.
>
> "Oh, no," Morris groaned. "I picked up the wrong bag. This is what my mom bought for my little brother. I don't have anything to eat."
>
> "You can have half of my peanut butter and jelly sandwich," said Pam.
>
> "Here, take some of these. I can't eat all these grapes," said Jeff.
>
> "I'll share my carton of juice with you," offered Jack.
>
> "Thanks, everybody," Morris said. "What teamwork!"

Problem-and-Solution Chart

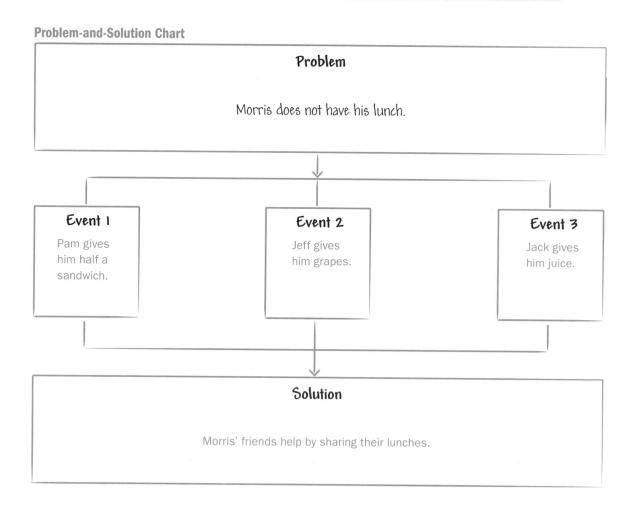

Problem

Morris does not have his lunch.

Event 1

Pam gives him half a sandwich.

Event 2

Jeff gives him grapes.

Event 3

Jack gives him juice.

Solution

Morris' friends help by sharing their lunches.

Name _____

High Frequency Words, Part 1

A. Read each word. Then write it.

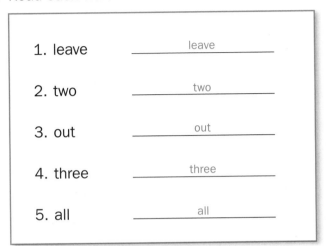

1. leave   _____leave_____

2. two   _____two_____

3. out   _____out_____

4. three   _____three_____

5. all   _____all_____

B. Work with a partner. Follow the steps.

- Read aloud each new word in the box.
- Your partner writes the words.
- Have your partner read the words to you.
- Now you write the words on the lines below.
- Read the words to your partner.

6. _____

7. _____

8. _____

9. _____

10. _____

High Frequency Words, Part 2

A. Read each word. Then write it.

1. says   _____ says _____

2. second   _____ second _____

3. without   _____ without _____

4. enough   _____ enough _____

5. more   _____ more _____

B. Find the new words in the box. Write the words on the lines.

6. These 2 words begin with **s**.

_____ says _____   _____ second _____

C. Work with a partner. Follow the steps.

• Read aloud each new word in the box.

• Your partner writes the words.

• Have your partner read the words to you.

• Now you write the words on the lines below.

• Read the words to your partner.

7. _____

8. _____

9. _____

10. _____

11. _____

Words with Digraphs

A. Name each picture. Write the name.

1.

trash

2.

ring

3.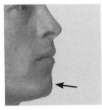

chin

4.

whisk

5.

ship

6.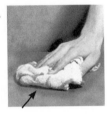

chess

7.

cloth

8.

bath

B. Now read the story. Circle the words that go in the chart. Write them in the chart. Write each word one time.

A Trip to (the) (Shop)

Dad and I go out to a (shop.) I (think) it sells great (shells.) We can (bring) some to Mom. I pick six (shells) and Dad pays (cash.) (There) is one more (thing) we want to do – find some (fresh) (fish) to eat. When we go home, Dad gives Mom (the) (shells.) Mom loves (them) and puts (them) on a (shelf.) What a great day!

Starts with *th*		Starts with *sh*	
9. the		16. Shop	
10. think		17. shells	
11. There		18. shelf	
12. thing			
13. them			
Ends with *ng*		**Ends with *sh***	
14. bring		19. cash	
15. thing		20. fresh	
		21. fish	

Words with Blends and Digraphs

A. Name each picture. Write the name.

1.

check

2.

lamp

3.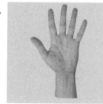

hand

4.

chick

5.

fish

6.

ant

B. Now read the story. Circle the words that go in the chart. Write them in the chart. Write each word one time.

Sal's Big (Trunk)

Sal has a big (trunk). He fills it with things.

Open the (trunk) and look in. You will see five

(clocks), sixteen red caps, a (brush) for a cat, and

ten tops. You will see a (chess) set, a little (lamp),

a (belt), twenty rocks, and (bath) stuff.

Do you like Sal's (trunk)? We can (shut) the

(trunk) now.

Starts with *tr*	Ends with *mp*
7. ___trunk___	11. ___lamp___
Starts with *cl*	**Ends with *lt***
8. ___clocks___	12. ___belt___
Starts with *sh*	**Ends with *sh***
9. ___shut___	13. ___brush___
Starts with *ch*	**Ends with *th***
10. ___chess___	14. ___bath___

Language and Literacy

Name _____

Words with Blends

A. Name each picture. Write the name.

1.
spots

2.
stamp

3.
drum

4.
flag

5.
disk

6.
frog

7.
sled

8.
plant

B. Now read the story. Circle the words that go in the chart. Write them in the chart. Write each word one time.

Pack for (Camp)

Jim packs his bag for (camp.) He needs enough (stuff) to (last) 5 days.

He packs:

- 1 (tent) and a mat to sleep on
- 2 swim (trunks) for his swim (class)
- a (belt,) 4 (snacks,) 10 socks, 1 brush, and more!

He can smash it all in the bag, but he can not lift the bag! Jim has to pack two bags for (camp.)

Starts with *st*	Ends with *st*
9. _____ stuff _____	13. _____ last _____
Starts with *tr*	**Ends with *nt***
10. _____ trunks _____	14. _____ tent _____
Starts with *cl*	**Ends with *mp***
11. _____ class _____	15. _____ Camp _____
Starts with *sn*	**Ends with *lt***
12. _____ snacks _____	16. _____ belt _____

Build Reading Fluency

▶ Phrasing

A. When you read, pause between groups of words that go together.

Stan is in / a big rush. //
Stan has three minutes / to catch his plane. //

B. Listen to the story. When you hear a short pause, write a / . When you hear a long pause, write //.

Rush!//

Stan is in/a big rush.//His plane leaves/at 2:00 p.m.//The clock says / 1:57 p.m.//Stan has three minutes / to catch his plane.//That is not/very long!/He jumps out of the cab/and slams the door. Bang!/He drops his bag.//All of his things/fall out of the bag.//Then he drops one more thing—his ticket!/A man helps Stan. //

The first thing he picks up/is the bag.//

The second thing he picks up/is the ticket.//The man asks Stan,/"When does your plane leave?"//

Stan says,/"I think it just left/ without me."//

The man looks at Stan's ticket.//

He grins/and tells Stan,/"You have enough time./Your plane leaves tomorrow/at two. //

C. Now read the story to a partner. Read groups of words together. Pause when you see a /.

I Don't Want This Food!

▶ **Contractions with *not***

A. When you make a contraction, you join two words together.

is + not = isn't	do + not = don't
are + not = aren't	does + not = doesn't

Use these contractions in negative sentences.

The food on the plane **isn't** very good.
The cookies **aren't** big.
The cake **doesn't** have nuts.
I **don't** want anything to eat.

B. Read each sentence. Change the underlined words to a contraction. Then complete the new sentence.

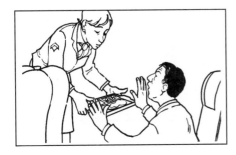

1. He <u>is not</u> happy.
   He ___isn't___ happy.

2. He does not like the food.
   He ___doesn't___ like the food.

3. She <u>does not</u> eat the cake.
   She ___doesn't___ eat the cake.

4. The cake <u>is not</u> sweet.
   The cake ___isn't___ sweet.

5. They <u>do not</u> want to eat.
   They ___don't___ want to eat.

6. They <u>are not</u> hungry.
   They ___aren't___ hungry.

Name _____

The Mighty Maya: Key Vocabulary

A. Study each word. Circle a number to rate how well you know it. Then complete the chart.

▲ This building was made **thousands** of years ago.

Rating Scale	**1** I have never seen this word before.	**2** I am not sure of the word's meaning.	**3** I know this word and can teach the word's meaning to someone else.

Key Words	Check Understanding	Deepen Understanding
❶ city (si-tē) *noun* Rating: 1 2 3	A **city** is very small with few people. Yes (No)	What city is close to you? *Responses will vary but should name a nearby city.*
❷ hundreds (**hun**-dridz) *noun* Rating: 1 2 3	An hour has **hundreds** of minutes. Yes (No)	Name a place where you can see hundreds of people. *Responses will vary. Possible responses are a mall, school, or a sports game.*
❸ population (pop-yū-lā-shun) *noun* Rating: 1 2 3	**Population** tells how many people live in one area. (Yes) No	Name a state with a big population. *Responses will vary. Possible responses are California, Texas, and New York.*

Name _____

These **two** men are Mayan. ▶

Key Words	Check Understanding	Deepen Understanding
❹ thousands (**thou**-zundz) *noun* **Rating:** 1 2 3	Texas has **thousands** of people. (Yes) No	Name a number in the thousands. *Responses will vary but should name a number in the thousands.*
❺ two (tū) *adjective* **Rating:** 1 2 3	A bike has **two** wheels. (Yes) No	Name two different holidays. *Responses will vary but should name two holidays.*

B. Use at least two of the Key Vocabulary words. Describe the population of your class. Is it large or small?

Answers will vary.

_____

_____

_____

Name _____

Plan and Write

1. What country will you research? _____

2. What do you want to know? Make a list.

   _____   _____

   _____   _____

   _____   _____

3. Choose your focus. Check three items.

4. Turn your list into questions. Write the questions. Research in books or on the Internet to find the answers to your questions. Write your answers. Draw a map of your country in the box at the top.

Facts About _____

- How large is _____

  The country of _____

  is _____

- What is the _____

  _____

  _____

  _____

- What is _____

  _____

  _____

  _____

A map of _____

Check Your Work

► Capitalization and End Marks

Read the fact sheet. Fix capital letters and add end punctuation as needed.
Mark your changes. Then write the questions and answers correctly.

Facts About Mexico

A map of Mexico

- How large is mexico?

  How large is Mexico?

mexico is about 742,485 square miles.

  Mexico is about 742,485 square miles.

- What is the population of mexico?

  What is the population of Mexico?

The population of Mexico is 108,700,891.

  The population of Mexico is 108,700,891.

- What is the longest river in mexico?

  What is the longest river in Mexico?

The rio grande is the longest river in Mexico.

  The Rio Grande is the longest river in Mexico.

- What is the population of the capital city of mexico?

  What is the population of the capital city of Mexico?

The capital city is Mexico city. The population of mexico city is 19,013,000.

  The capital city is Mexico City. The population of Mexico City is 19,013,000.

Mind Map

Use the mind map to show how to find out about your town or city. As you read the selections in this unit, add new ideas for ways to learn about a city.

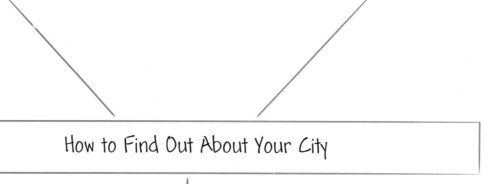

How to Find Out About Your City

Language Development

Where Is It?

▶ **Language: Ask For and Give Information**

▶ **Vocabulary: Location Words**

A. Study the places.

Location Words

in

on

by, near

above, over

below, under

next to, beside

between

down

behind, in back of

B. Complete each sentence. Tell where the places are. Use location words.

1. The pet shop is _____ on _____ the corner.

2. You can get dog food _____ in _____ the pet shop.

3. The toy store is _____ above / over _____ the café.

4. The toy store is _____ between _____ the music store and the market.

5. You go _____ down _____ the stairs to get from the market to the bakery.

6. The market is _____ above / over _____ the bakery.

7. The café is _____ next to / beside _____ the bakery.

8. There are two plants _____ by / near _____ the café.

9. There is someone _____ behind / in back of _____ the door to the bakery.

10. The theater is _____ below / under _____ the pet shop.

Language Development

Things in the Neighborhood

▶ **Vocabulary: Neighborhood**

▶ **Language: Ask For and Give Information**

A. Name each place. Then name something you see there. Use words from the box.

intersection	post office	bus station	store	bus	parking lot	mailbox	stop sign

1.

bus station

3.

intersection

2.

store

4.

post office

B. Answer each question. Use a complete sentence.

Answers will vary. Sample responses are given.

5. What happens at the bus station?

   People wait for the bus.

6. What happens at the intersection?

   People walk across the street. They walk on the crosswalk.

7. What happens at the store?

   People buy food.

8. What happens at the post office?

   People mail letters.

Language Development

On My Street

▶ Grammar: Regular Past Tense Verbs

A verb changes to show the past tense.

She **cooks** the food.

She **cooked** the food.

Look at each picture. Read the sentence. Circle the correct verb.

1.

They _____ play /(played)_____ soccer.

2.

She _____ parks /(parked)_____ her car.

3.

He _____ opens /(opened)_____ the bag of chips.

4.

She _____ (adds)/ added_____ flowers to the garden.

5.

He _____ (cleans)/ cleaned_____ the car.

6.

They _____ help /(helped)_____ win the game.

Language Development

We Visited the Zoo

► Regular Past Tense Verbs

You can add *–ed* to many verbs to tell about things that happened in the past.

We **wanted** to go to the city zoo.

I **asked** Mom to take us there.

Complete each sentence. Add the past tense of the verb in dark type.

1. We _____walked_____ around the zoo.
   (walk)

2. Sam _____watched_____ the young lions.
   (watch)

3. They _____looked_____ so big!
   (look)

4. Tara _____stayed_____ away from them!
   (stay)

5. I _____asked_____ to see the monkeys.
   (ask)

6. They _____jumped_____ all around.
   (jump)

7. One monkey _____tossed_____ a ball.
   (toss)

8. We _____listened_____ to them yell!
   (listen)

9. Mom _____laughed_____ .
   (laugh)

10. We all _____enjoyed_____ our visit.
    (enjoy)

Language Development

Identify Details

▶ **Sum It Up**

A. Read what Sergio did in his neighborhood. Make a detail chart to show what he did and when he did it. The first row in the chart has been filled in for you.

> **Sergio's Busy Week**
>
> Sergio has many nice neighbors. He spent a lot of time this week helping them after school. On Monday, Sergio shopped for dog treats. Then he walked Mrs. Perez's dog. On Tuesday, he mowed the grass for Mr. Mendez. He read the paper to Mr. Mendez, too. On Wednesday, Sergio carried groceries for Mrs. Gold. Then he stacked groceries on her kitchen shelves. On Thursday, Sergio watched Mrs. Lee's twin boys. On Friday, Sergio played baseball after school. All the neighbors went to the game and cheered for him!

Detail Chart

Day	Events
Monday	shopped for dog treats, walked dog
Tuesday	mowed grass, read paper
Wednesday	carried groceries, stacked groceries
Thursday	watched twin boys
Friday	played baseball

B. Imagine that you are one of Sergio's neighbors. Write a thank-you note to thank him for helping you.

Answers will vary.

Dear Sergio,

Thank you for _____

_____

_____

Your neighbor,

_____

Language and Literacy

High Frequency Words, Part 1

A. Read each word. Then write it.

1. city   _____city_____

2. above   _____above_____

3. by   _____by_____

4. sometimes _____sometimes_____

5. her   _____her_____

B. Read each sentence. Find the new words in the box. Write the words on the lines.

6. These 2 words end with **y.**

     _____city_____   _____by_____

7. These 2 words are location words.

     _____above_____   _____by_____

8. This word rhymes with **my.**

     _____by_____

9. This word has 2 smaller words in it.

     _____sometimes_____

10. This word has **er.**

     _____her_____

Language and Literacy

High Frequency Words, Part 2

A. Read each word. Then write it.

1. come   _____come_____

2. animals   _____animals_____

3. people   _____people_____

4. down   _____down_____

5. under   _____under_____

B. Read each sentence. Find the new words in the box. Write the words on the lines.

6. This word starts with **c**.

   _____come_____

7. These 2 words name living things.

   _____animals_____   _____people_____

8. These 2 words are location words.

   _____down_____   _____under_____

9. These 2 words end with **e**.

   _____come_____   _____people_____

10. This word has **er**.

   _____under_____

Words with Long and Short Vowels

A. Name each picture. Read the two words. Circle the word that names the picture.

1.

(face)/ fact

2.

hi / (hill)

3.

be /(bell)

4.

(wet)/ we

B. Now read the story. Circle the words with long e. Then circle the words with short e. Write them in the chart. Write each word one time.

(We) Like to Swim!

(We) like to swim. But I do not like to (get)(wet)! The pool is near my home. I walk there with Kim. (She) is my friend. (We) can (be) in the water until the (bell) rings. (Then)(we) have to (get) out. As (we) wait, I (get) dry. (When) they (let) us back in the pool, I (get)(wet) again! I like to swim so much that I do not mind if I (get)(wet). Kim (bet)(me) I would like swimming more if I could stay dry, but I cannot do that! (She) is funny.

Words with long e	Words with short e
5. _____ we _____	9. _____ get _____
6. _____ she _____	10. _____ wet _____
7. _____ be _____	11. _____ bell _____
8. _____ me _____	12. _____ then _____
	13. _____ when _____
	14. _____ let _____
	15. _____ bet _____

Words with Long and Short Vowels

A. Name each picture. Read the two words. Circle the word that names the picture.

1.

he /(hen)

2.

(he)/ help

3.

(hi)/ hit

4.

be /(bell)

B. Now read the story. Circle the words with long e. Then circle the words with short e. Write them in the chart. Write each word one time.

At Home in the City

I like my home in the city. On Saturdays, Sal and I (help) at the library. (He) sits at the (desk.) I show the kids good books. (Then) I (let) (them) look around without (me.) At 12:00, (we) are done. Sometimes (we) stop for lunch. (Then) (we) go home. (We) walk down Grand Road. The city is so great! (We) can (be) home in two minutes.

Words with long e	Words with short e
5. ____he____	9. ____help____
6. ____me____	10. ____desk____
7. ____we____	11. ____Then____
8. ____be____	12. ____let____
	13. ____them____

Name _____

Multisyllabic Words

A. Read each word. Write how many syllables it has.

1.
pool

_____1_____

2.
nickel

_____2_____

3.
moon

_____1_____

4.
garden

_____2_____

5.
basket

_____2_____

6.
napkin

_____2_____

7.
screw

_____1_____

8.
broom

_____1_____

B. Now read the story. Circle the words with two syllables. Write each word in the chart. Then write the syllables.

Hunting a Pumpkin

We went to find a pumpkin at the farm. We wanted the biggest one in the field. My sister helped me look. We saw a lot of pumpkins. We also saw a snake! My mom was calling to us. The farmer told us to look in the far corner of the field. There we saw the biggest pumpkin in the whole field! Next to it was a small one. We could not carry the big pumpkin, so we picked the small one.

Word	Syllable	
9. hunting	hunt	ing
10. pumpkin	pump	kin
11. wanted	want	ed
12. biggest	big	gest
13. sister	sis	ter
14. also	al	so
15. calling	call	ing
16. farmer	farm	er
17. corner	cor	ner
18. carry	car	ry

Name _____

Multisyllabic Words

A. Read each word. Write how many syllables it has.

1.

basket

_____2_____

2.

pumpkin

_____2_____

3.

egg

_____1_____

4.

muffin

_____2_____

5.

stamp

_____1_____

6.

plate

_____1_____

7.

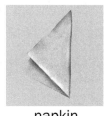

napkin

_____2_____

8.

bench

_____1_____

B. Now read the story. Circle the words with two syllables. Write each word in the chart. Then write the syllables.

A (Picnic) in the Park

Jan and Chun go on a (picnic.) Jan packs

lunch in a (basket.) Chun grabs a (blanket.) Then

they put on their (helmets) and hop on their

bikes. They ride through a (tunnel,) then up to

Elm Road. They watch out for (traffic.) At the

park, they see lots of (children.) Chun puts the

(blanket) on the grass, and they sit down. "Let's

eat," Jan says. "Do you want a (sandwich?)"

Word	Syllable	
9. _____picnic_____	pic	nic
10. _____basket_____	bas	ket
11. _____blanket_____	blan	ket
12. _____helmets_____	hel	mets
13. _____tunnel_____	tun	nel
14. _____traffic_____	traf	fic
15. _____children_____	chil	dren
16. _____sandwich_____	sand	wich

Build Reading Fluency

▶ Expression

A. Some sentences tell something. Other sentences show strong feeling.

This sentence tells something. It ends with a period.

> Jo works at the City Animal Hospital .

This sentence shows a strong feeling.
It ends with an exclamation mark.

> He is so soft !

B. Listen to the different kinds of sentences.

Meet Jo

Jo works at the City Animal Hospital. I asked her to tell me about what she does at her job.

I have a great job. I love to help the animals. Look. This cat got hit by traffic. It is so sad when that happens. I had to make her a special bed. She has to lie down a lot.

This is Samson. Samson has a bad rash. He has this thing around his neck so he can't bite the skin under it. Sometimes we play catch.

He needs to run a lot. He likes to run down the hill to the park. We rest under the trees. I like to look at the sky above us as Samson sleeps.

This rabbit is Velvet. I like to brush him. He is so soft! Velvet had to get his shots. He needs to rest for a day or two. Then he will go home.

So, that is my job. I help hundreds of animals. It is great to see them get well. I miss them when people come to take them home.

C. Now read the sentences to a partner. See how your reading improves!

They're from My Neighborhood

▶ Pronoun-Verb Contractions

A. You can put a pronoun and a verb together to form a contraction.

I + am = I'm	**I'm** on the sidewalk.
you + are = you're	**You're** slow.
he + is = he's she + is = she's it + is = it's	**It's** a sunny day.
we + are = we're	**We're** glad to be together.
they + are = they're	**They're** in the park.

B. Combine the words in dark type to make a contraction. Use the contraction to complete the sentence.

1. Sam and Kim are Mia's friends. _____They're_____ her neighbors.
   (They are)

2. Mia walks the dogs for Sam and Kim. _____She's_____ happy to do it.
   (She is)

3. One dog stops to rest. _____He's_____ a small dog.
   (He is)

4. Mia laughs at the dog. "_____You're_____ slow, Biff."
   (You are)

5. "You can rest, Biff. _____We're_____ not in a hurry."
   (We are)

6. Mia waits for Biff. _____She's_____ nice to all the dogs.
   (She is)

7. People look at the dogs. _____They're_____ surprised to see so many!
   (They are)

8. Soon the walk is over. _____It's_____ time to eat.
   (It is)

Learn Key Vocabulary

San Francisco: Key Vocabulary

A. Study each word. Circle a number to rate how well you know it. Then complete the chart.

▲ The city of San Francisco has many tall **buildings**.

Rating Scale	**1** I have never seen this word before.	**2** I am not sure of the word's meaning.	**3** I know this word and can teach the word's meaning to someone else.

Key Words	Check Understanding	Deepen Understanding
❶ buildings (bil-dings) *noun* **Rating:** 1 2 3	Houses are **buildings**. (Yes) No	What makes buildings look good? *Responses will vary but could relate to paint colors, windows, roofs, or landscaping.* _____ _____ _____
❷ live (liv) *verb* **Rating:** 1 2 3	Many people **live** in cities. (Yes) No	Where would you like to live? *Responses will vary but should relate to different places to live.* _____ _____ _____
❸ neighborhood (nā-bor-hood) *noun* **Rating:** 1 2 3	A **neighborhood** is made up of homes and shops. (Yes) No	Describe your neighborhood. *Responses will vary. Possible responses could relate to homes and stores where students live.* _____ _____ _____

Key Vocabulary, continued

San Francisco was once a small **town** with only a few **buildings** like this one. ▶

Key Words	Check Understanding	Deepen Understanding
❹ store (stor) *noun* **Rating:** 1 2 3	You can buy things at a **store**. (Yes) No	Describe a store near you. *Responses will vary but should relate to a nearby store.* _____ _____ _____
❺ town (toun) *noun* **Rating:** 1 2 3	A **town** and a city are the same size. Yes (No)	Tell about a town that you have visited. *Responses will vary but should describe a town and its features.* _____ _____ _____

B. Use at least two of the Key Vocabulary words. Tell what makes your neighborhood special.

Answers will vary.

_____

_____

_____

Plan and Write

Answers will vary. Check that students have filled in the chart and completed each sentence below.

1. Think about things you did last week. Complete the chart.

Day	Events	Place
Monday		
Tuesday		
Wednesday		
Thursday		
Friday		
Saturday		
Sunday		

2. Use your notes to write a journal page. Use past tense verbs.

Last Monday, I _____

On Tuesday, _____

On Wednesday, _____

On Thursday, _____

On Friday, _____

On Saturday, _____

On Sunday, _____

Check Your Work

► Capitalization and End Marks

Read this journal page. Fix capital letters and add end punctuation as needed. Mark your changes. Then write each sentence correctly.

Mark Your Changes

∧ Add.

≡ Capitalize.

Last monday, i played baseball in the park

Last Monday, I played baseball in the park.

On tuesday, I looked for books in the library

On Tuesday, I looked for books in the library.

On wednesday, i shopped at the mall

On Wednesday, I shopped at the mall.

On Thursday, i went to dinner in a restaurant

On Thursday, I went to dinner in a restaurant.

On friday, I visited my friend at her house

On Friday, I visited my friend at her house.

On saturday, I cleaned my bedroom

On Saturday, I cleaned my bedroom.

On sunday, i cooked breakfast in my kitchen

On Sunday, I cooked breakfast in my kitchen.

Mind Map

Use the mind map to show what you know about family life. As you read the selections in this unit, add new ideas you learn about the people, places, and events that are part of family life.

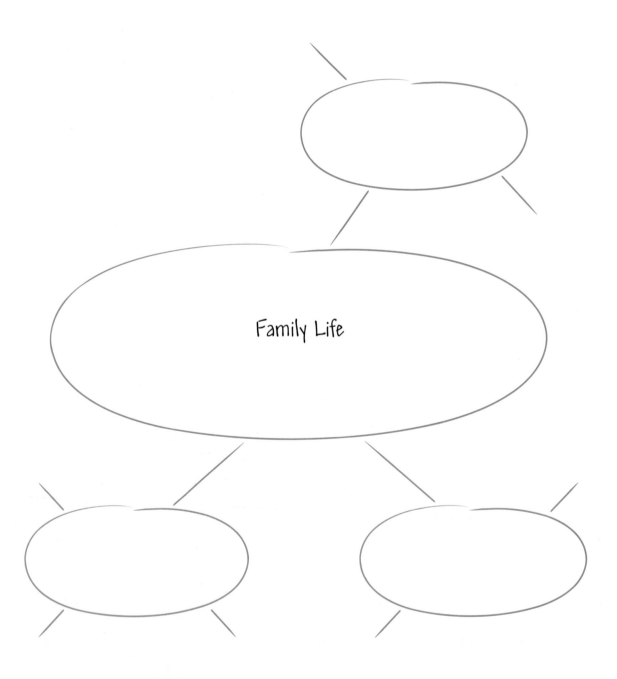

Family Life

Meet Lin's Family

▶ **Language: Give Information**
▶ **Vocabulary: Family**

Remind students that some family words may appear more than once in the family tree.

Family Words

grandfather	brother
grandmother	sister
father	uncle
mother	aunt

A. Use family words to tell about Lin's family tree. Then answer the question below.

grandfather   grandmother   grandfather   grandmother

father   mother

brother   Lin   sister

Lin's Family Tree

B. How many people are in Lin's family? _____ Nine _____ of them together make up Lin's family tree.

I Have a Great Family

▶ **Grammar: Present Tense Verbs: *Have* and *Has***

Use *have* with *I, you, we,* and *they.* Use *has* with *he, she,* or *it.*

Hi. I'm Rita. I **have** a sister. We **have** a new brother. He **has** a room. It **has** toys in it.

Complete each sentence. Use *have* or *has.*

1.

"I _____have_____ an aunt."

"She _____has_____ a dog."

2.

"We _____have_____ a small house."

"The house _____has_____ trees around it."

3.

He _____has_____ a sister.

They _____have_____ fun together.

4.

He _____has_____ an uncle.

His uncle _____has_____ a big bike.

What Is in Each Room?

▶ **Vocabulary: Household Objects**

▶ **Language: Ask and Answer Questions**

A. Name the things in each room. Use words from the box.

bathtub	bed	lamp	oven
couch	dresser	sink	shower
stove	rug	refrigerator	door

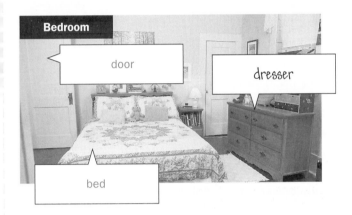

Bedroom — door, dresser, bed

Bathroom — shower, sink, bathtub

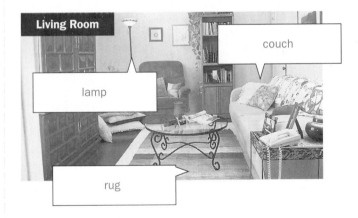

Living Room — couch, lamp, rug

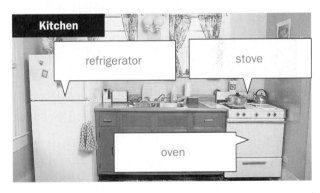

Kitchen — refrigerator, stove, oven

B. Answer each question. Use a complete sentence.

Responses will vary.
Sample responses are given.

1. Where is the couch? The couch is in the living room.

2. Where is the dresser? The dresser is in the bedroom.

3. Where is the oven? The oven is in the kitchen.

C. Write two questions. Ask about two things in the rooms above.

4. Where is the shower?

5. Where is the lamp?

Identify Details that Support a Main Idea

▶ **Sum It Up**

Read the following article. Read the main idea. Write the important ideas in the Main Idea Diagram.

Chinese Family Traditions

Families that lived a long time ago in China had many traditions. Grandparents lived with one of their children and helped take care of the grandchildren. Then as the grandparents got older, their children and grandchildren took care of them. Babies were often named after family members from older generations. Holidays such as the Chinese New Year were celebrated with family members. Younger people showed respect to older people. The older people gave gifts to the youngsters. When it was time to marry, the parents or grandparents chose a husband or wife for their child. The Chinese believed that their traditions made strong families.

Answers will vary. Sample responses are given.

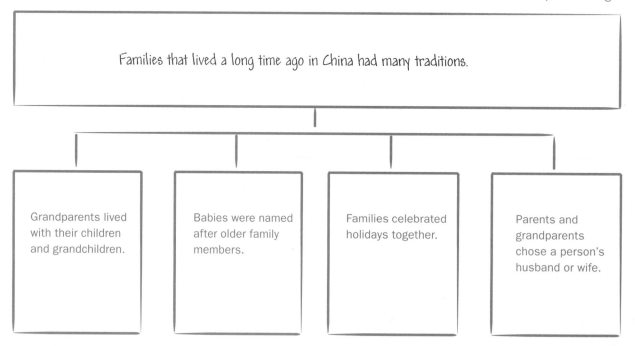

Families that lived a long time ago in China had many traditions.

| Grandparents lived with their children and grandchildren. | Babies were named after older family members. | Families celebrated holidays together. | Parents and grandparents chose a person's husband or wife. |

Language and Literacy

High Frequency Words, Part 1

A. Read each word. Then write it.

1. family _____family_____

2. together _____together_____

3. other _____other_____

4. really _____really_____

5. father _____father_____

B. Read the clue. Write the word in the chart. Then write the word again in the sentence.

What to Look For	Word	Sentence
6. begins with **fam**	f a m i l y	My ___family___ loves games.
7. begins with **to**	t o g e t h e r	We like to be ___together___ .
8. begins with **o**	o t h e r	We do ___other___ things, too.
9. begins with **r**	r e a l l y	We have a ___really___ big family.
10. means "dad"	f a t h e r	My ___father___ is an artist.

High Frequency Words, Part 2

A. Read each word. Then write it.

1. mother _____mother_____

2. our _____our_____

3. watch _____watch_____

4. eyes _____eyes_____

5. head _____head_____

B. Read the clue. Write the word in the chart. Then write the word again in the sentence.

What to Look For	Word	Sentence
6. means "mom"	m o t h e r	My _____mother_____ is a writer.
7. has 3 letters	o u r	Friday is _____our_____ game night.
8. ends with **tch**	w a t c h	Sometimes we _____watch_____ TV.
9. has **yes** in it	e y e s	I use my _____eyes_____ to do puzzles.
10. rhymes with **bed**	h e a d	I think with my _____head_____ .

Words with Long Vowels: *a_e, o_e*

A. Name each picture. Write the name.

1.
tape

2.
stage

3.
vase

4.
cake

5.
rope

6.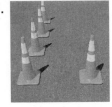
cones

7.
globe

8.
phone

B. Now read the story. Circle the words with long *a* or long *o*. Write them in the chart. Write each word one time.

Trouble at the (Lake)

Our (home) is (close) to a (lake) The (lake) is big. Sometimes it has big (waves).

One day I (take) a ride and get to the (lake) I (gaze) out. (Those) (waves) are big! I see a boy in trouble. A man comes by and spots the boy. He jumps into the water and swims out with big (strokes) I shut my eyes and (hope) he can (save) the boy. And he does!

I (spoke) to the man. "That was very (brave)!" I said.

9. ____Lake____	15. ____home____
10. ____waves____	16. ____close____
11. ____take____	17. ____Those____
12. ____gaze____	18. ____strokes____
13. ____save____	19. ____hope____
14. ____brave____	20. ____spoke____

Words with Long Vowels

A. Name each picture. Write the name.

1.
cape

2.
bike

3.
globe

4.
mule

5.
robe

6.
cake

7.
kite

8.
tube

B. Now read the story. Circle the words with long *a, i, o,* or *u*. Write them in the chart. Write each word one time.

Fun with Bill

My brother Bill (drives) a truck all around the

(state.) When he is (home), he (makes) (life) fun.

Once he put together (kites) for all the kids in

the family. Bill had to (use) long, thin (tubes) for

the (frames.) The wings were cloth from a torn

(robe.) "The (kites) are (cute)," he said, "but I (hope)

we can get them up in the air!"

9. state	15. home
10. makes	16. robe
11. frames	17. hope
12. drives	18. use
13. life	19. tubes
14. kites	20. cute

Language and Literacy

Name _____

Words with Short and Long Vowels

A. Name each picture. Read the two words. Circle the word that names the picture.

1.
(cap)/ cape

2.
(pill)/ pile

3.
kit /(kite)

4.
(tub)/ tube

5.
rob /(robe)

6.
(cut)/ cute

7.
(rod)/ rode

8.
tap /(tape)

B. Now read the story. Circle the words with long *o* or long *i*. Underline the words with short *o* or short *i*. Write them in the chart. Write each word one time.

A Busy (Home)

We are really busy. Here <u>is</u> what a day <u>is</u> (like). Mom (drives) to the pet <u>shop</u>. She must be there by three. The <u>shop</u> (closes) at three. Then Mom <u>stops</u> to get us snacks to eat. Dad helps me <u>fix</u> my (bike), and then we scrub the (stove). Pam has to watch the baby next door. At the end of the day, we (like) to <u>sit</u> down and rest. That <u>is</u> when we can all be together again.

9. Home	15. Mom
10. closes	16. shop
11. stove	17. stops
12. like	18. is
13. drives	19. fix
14. bike	20. sit

© NGSP & HB

Unit 6 Welcome Home! 97

Plurals

A. Name each picture. Read the two words. Circle the word that names the picture.

1.
boy / (boys)

2.
state / (states)

3.
pin / (pins)

4.
duck / (ducks)

5.
stripe / (stripes)

6.
(pear) / pears

7.
(tray) / trays

8.
(star) / stars

B. Now read the story. Circle the words that name more than one thing. Write them in the chart. Write each word one time.

(Parades) in the City

Our city has many (parades) for (kids). The (parades) are a lot of fun. (Girls) and (boys) pass by in (bands). They play (drums) and (trumpets) and other (things). (Girls) do (tricks) with (batons). We see (costumes) with a lot of (colors). We see many (pets), too. (Boys) and (girls) pass by with their (dogs), (cats), and (snakes). (Parents) stand on the sidewalk and clap. They like to see the (kids).

Plurals	
9. _parades_	18. _batons_
10. _kids_	19. _costumes_
11. _girls_	20. _colors_
12. _boys_	21. _pets_
13. _bands_	22. _dogs_
14. _drums_	23. _cats_
15. _trumpets_	24. _snakes_
16. _things_	25. _parents_
17. _tricks_	

Build Reading Fluency

▶ **Phrasing**

A. When you read, pause between groups of words that go together.

In Nicaragua, / my family made / big puppets to sell. //
We made the arms / from long tubes. //

B. Listen to the story. When you hear a short pause, write a / . When you hear a long pause, write //.

Example: In Nicaragua, / my family made / big puppets to sell.//

When We Came to Wisconsin

Hi.//My name is Pablo Soto.//My mother's name is Sandra.//We are from Nicaragua.//

In Nicaragua,/our family made/big puppets to sell.//The name of one puppet that we made/is *La Gigantona*.//We made the head of this puppet/with paper and paste.//We made the eyes of the puppet/really big,/with long,/thick lashes.//We made the arms/from long tubes.//They swing/from side to side.//We put a white robe,/a cute hat,/and other things/on the puppet.//People like to watch this big puppet/in parades.//

C. Now read the story to a partner. Use the marks you made to read groups of words together.

Name _____

New Neighbors

▶ Plural Nouns

A. A noun names a person, place, or thing.

A singular noun names one thing.

box

A plural noun names more than one thing.

boxes

Study these rules for forming plurals.

To make most nouns plural, just add **-s**.	boy boys	girl girls	book books
If the noun ends in **x, ch, sh, s,** or **z**, add **-es**.	box boxes	dish dishes	glass glasses
Some nouns change in different ways.	man men	woman women	child children

B. Complete each sentence. Use the plural form of the word in dark type.

1. Two ___women___ bring food.
   (woman)

2. There are many ___boxes___ to unpack.
   (box)

3. Mrs. Lee finds the ___dishes___ .
   (dish)

4. Then she finds the ___cups___ .
   (cup)

5. They eat their ___lunches___ .
   (lunch)

6. Mrs. Lee has two new ___friends___ .
   (friend)

Name _____

The Family Reunion: Key Vocabulary

A. Study each word. Circle a number to rate how well you know it. Then complete the chart.

Rating Scale	**1** I have never seen this word before.	**2** I am not sure of the word's meaning.	**3** I know this word and can teach the word's meaning to someone else.

▲ This **family** is **together** at a party.

Key Words	Check Understanding	Deepen Understanding
❶ cousins (**ku**-zinz) *noun* Rating: 1 2 3	My **cousins** are my mother's sisters. Yes (No)	How are cousins related to each other? *Responses will vary but should reflect students'* *understanding of the relationship of cousins.*
❷ family (**fa**-mu-lē) *noun* Rating: 1 2 3	A **family** can be big or small. (Yes) No	Name at least two people in your family. *Responses will vary but should refer to at least two* *family members.*
❸ grandchildren (**grand**-chil-drun) *noun* Rating: 1 2 3	Grandparents can have many **grandchildren**. (Yes) No	Tell about the grandchildren in your family. *Responses will vary but should refer to grandchildren in* *the family.*

Name _____

These **parents** like to play music with their children.

Key Words	Check Understanding	Deepen Understanding
❹ parents (**pair**-ents) *noun* **Rating:** 1 2 3	Your brother and sister are your **parents**. Yes (No)	Name something parents do for children. *Responses will vary. Possible responses include help them with homework, take them to school, or make them meals.*
❺ together (tu-**ge**-thur) *adverb* **Rating:** 1 2 3	Children often play **together**. (Yes) No	What do you and your family do together? *Responses will vary but should identify one or more activities students do with family members.*

B. Use at least two of the Key Vocabulary words. Explain why it is important for family and friends to be together.

Answers will vary.

_____

_____

_____

Name _____

Plan and Write

Answers will vary. Check that students have focused each description on one person and have told what each person likes and does.

1. Choose two people to write about. Write their names in the first column. Then fill in the chart.

Who?	What the Person Likes	What the Person Does	Where	Something Special About the Person

2. Write a title and your name.

3. Write 3 complete sentences about each person. Tell
   - what the person **likes**
   - what the person **has** and **where** it is
   - **something special** about the person

_____

by _____

My _____ likes _____ .

_____ has _____ .

_____ is _____ .

Name _____

Check Your Work

Added details will vary.

▶ Plurals and Details

Read the descriptions. Fix plural nouns as needed. Mark your changes.
Then write the sentences correctly.

My Family

by Sara Thomas

Uncle Jackson likes ⌄old⌄ trucks. He has two 1969 truck⌄ˢ in his garage. He fixes broken car⌄ˢ and

truck⌄ˢ.

Uncle Jackson likes old trucks. He has two 1969 trucks in his garage. He fixes broken cars and trucks.

_____

_____

My sister Ramona likes playing in the park. She has a collection of toy car⌄ˢ Ramona

can whistle.

My sister Ramona likes playing in the park. She has a collection of toy cars. Ramona can whistle.

_____

_____

My brother Stuart likes to cook. He has his own pots and pan⌄ˢ He is a ⌄good⌄ cook.

My brother Stuart likes to cook. He has his own pots and pans. He is a good cook.

_____

_____

My cousins like to play guitar. They have ⌄lots of⌄ instrument⌄ˢ They know many song⌄ˢ.

My cousins like to play guitar. They have lots of instruments. They know many songs.

_____

_____

Name _____

Mind Map

Use the mind map to show what you know about the rain forest. As you read the selections in this unit, add new ideas you learn about the plants, animals, and landforms of the rain forest.

Pack Your Bags — for the Rain Forest!

Plants	Animals	Landforms	What to Pack

Give Commands

▶ **Language: Give and Carry Out Commands**

A. Study the commands.

Wear a jacket.	Get some warm clothes.	Find a seat.
Grab a camera.	Ride the bus.	Pack your bag.
Enjoy the trip!	Take some gloves.	Step on the bus.
Dress for snow.	Don't forget a hat.	Take some film.

B. Write two commands for each picture. Use commands from the box.

Answers will vary. Sample responses are given.

1.

Get some warm clothes.

Pack your bag.

_____

2.

Dress for snow.

Wear a jacket.

_____

3.

Don't forget a hat.

Take some gloves.

_____

4.

Grab a camera.

Take some film.

_____

5.

Step on the bus.

Find a seat.

_____

6.

Ride the bus.

Enjoy the trip!

_____

Language Development

What Do You See?

▶ **Vocabulary: Landforms and Transportation**

▶ **Language: Describe Places**

A. Name the places and things in the picture. Use words from the box.

ocean	forest	sailboat	airplane	beach	island

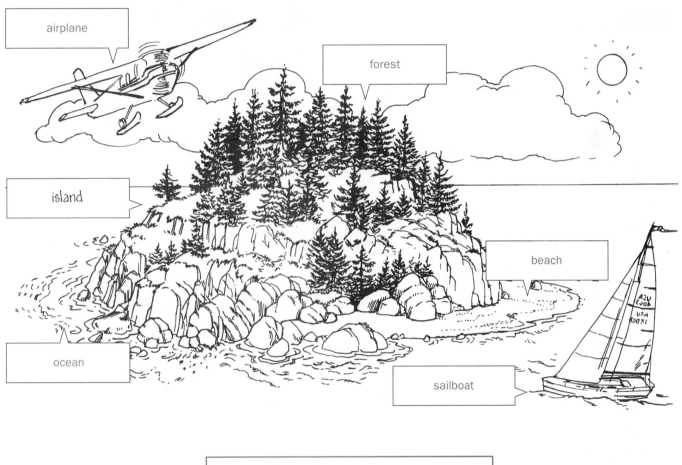

airplane

forest

island

beach

ocean

sailboat

small	tall	hot	dry	fast

B. Complete each sentence. Describe the picture above. Use adjectives from the box.

1. The island has a forest with _____ tall _____ trees.

2. A _____ fast / small _____ airplane flies over the island.

3. A _____ small / fast _____ sailboat sails on the ocean.

4. The _____ hot _____ sun shines on the beach.

5. It makes the sand hot and _____ dry _____ .

Name _____

What Do They Wear?

▶ **Vocabulary: Weather and Clothing**

▶ **Language: Give Information**

A. Name the things to wear. Use words from the box.

| sneaker | glove | scarf | bathing suit | sandal | parka |

Sunny and Warm

bathing suit

sandal

sneaker

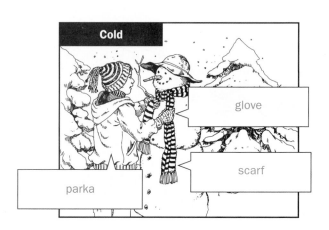

Cold

glove

scarf

parka

B. What is the weather like? Tell Brandon and Rachel what clothing to pack.

Answers will vary. Sample responses are given.

1. It is _____ sunny _____ and _____ warm _____ at the beach.

2. Take a _____ bathing suit _____ so you can swim.

3. Pack some _____ sneakers _____ to wear on your feet.

4. Wear your _____ sandals _____ when it is really hot.

5. It is _____ cold / windy _____ in the mountains.

6. Take a warm coat or _____ parka _____ .

7. Pack _____ gloves _____ to keep your hands warm.

8. Wear a _____ scarf _____ around your neck.

Language Development

Name _____

Yes, You Can!

▶ **Grammar: Use the Verb *Can***

Use *can* before another verb to tell what people are able to do.

| can | + | sail | = | can sail |

My father **can sail** a boat.

He **can take** my sister to an island.

She **can visit** her friends there.

Never add -s to *can*.

Complete each sentence. Tell what the people in each picture can do. Use *can* and a word from the box.

| work | wear | see | hike | ski | play | plant | swim |

winter

spring

summer

fall

1. In the winter, he _____can ski_____ in the mountains.

2. In the winter, he _____can play_____ in the snow.

3. In the spring, she _____can work_____ in the garden.

4. In the spring, she _____can plant_____ flowers.

5. In the summer, he _____can swim_____ in the pool.

6. In the summer, he _____can wear_____ a bathing suit.

7. In the fall, they _____can see_____ pretty trees.

8. In the fall, they _____can hike_____ in the park.

© NGSP & HB

Unit 7 Pack Your Bags!   **109**

Language Development

Classify Information

▶ Sum It Up

A. Think of a place you would like to explore. Write the name in the middle of the concept map below. Then write what you can see there, what the weather is like, and what you would wear.

Answers will vary. A possible response is given.

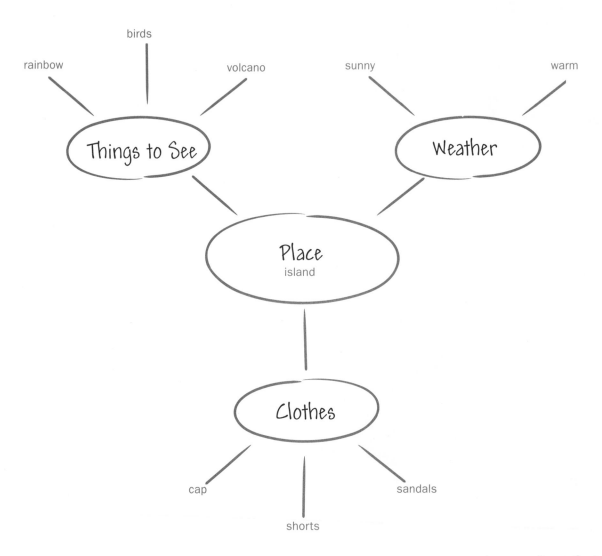

B. Write sentences to describe the place you would like to explore.

Answers will vary. Sentences should be based on information classified in the concept map.

_____

_____

_____

_____

_____

High Frequency Words, Part 1

A. Read each word. Then write it.

1. places   _____ places _____

2. important   _____ important _____

3. world   _____ world _____

4. always   _____ always _____

5. or   _____ or _____

B. Find the new words. Write the words on the lines.

6. These 2 words have a **w**.

_____ always _____   _____ world _____

C. Work with a partner. Follow the steps.

- Read aloud each new word in the box.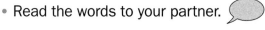

- Your partner writes the words.

- Have your partner read the words to you.

- Now you write the words on the lines below.

- Read the words to your partner.

    7. _____

    8. _____

    9. _____

   10. _____

   11. _____

High Frequency Words, Part 2

A. Read each word. Then write it.

1. river   _____river_____

2. through   _____through_____

3. once   _____once_____

4. water   _____water_____

5. below   _____below_____

B. Find the new words in the box. Write the words on the lines.

6. These 2 words have a **w**.

_____water_____   _____below_____

C. Work with a partner. Follow the steps.

• Read aloud each new word in the box.

• Your partner writes the words.

• Have your partner read the words to you.

• Now you write the words on the lines below.

• Read the words to your partner.

7. _____

8. _____

9. _____

10. _____

11. _____

Language and Literacy

Name _____

Words with Long *a*

A. Read each word. Which picture goes with the word? Write its letter.

1. tray ___D___   2. stain ___B___   3. play ___C___

4. sail ___A___   5. midday ___E___   6. train ___F___

A.    B.    C.

D.    E.   F.

B. Now read the story. Circle long *a* words with *ai* and *ay*. Write them in the chart. Write each word one time.

My Grandma's Chair

My grandma has a favorite chair. She (mainly) keeps it upstairs. It has blue and purple flowers in a (chain.) It is big and soft. When I was little, my grandma let me (play) in her chair. I would pretend to be an old lady.

My grandma has (gray) hair, but she likes to do many things. She loves to (raise) the window shades early in the (day.) Sometimes, my grandma and I collect (daisies.) Then she might (say,) "Now, you (may) sit in my special chair." I (always) (wait) for her to tell me.

7.	mainly	12.	play
8.	chain	13.	gray
9.	raise	14.	day
10.	daisies	15.	say
11.	wait	16.	may
		17.	always

© NGSP & HB

Unit 7 Pack Your Bags! **113**

Words with Long *a*, Long *e*, and Long *o*

A. Read each word. Which picture goes with the word? Write its letter.

1. coast __N__
2. boat __C__
3. train __F__
4. braid __I__
5. road __K__
6. seeds __L__
7. paints __B__
8. feet __D__
9. sail __A__
10. tree __G__
11. tray __E__
12. geese __H__
13. crow __M__
14. seal __O__
15. tea __J__

A.
B.
C.
D.
E.

F.
G.
H.
I.
J.

K.
L.
M.
N.
O.

B. Name each picture below. Which words above have the same long vowel sound as the picture name? Write the words on the lines.

16.
train
braid
paints
sail
tray

17.
seeds
feet
tree
geese
seal
tea

18.
coast
boat
road
crow

Name _____

Words with Short and Long Vowels

A. Name each picture. Read the two words. Circle the word that names the picture.

1.

cot / (coat)

2.

tap / (tail)

3.

(bed) / beach

4.

sell / (seal)

5.

(pan) / paint

6.

pens / (peas)

7.

cost / (coast)

8.

(rod) / road

B. Now read the story. Circle the words with long *a*. Underline the words with short *a*. Write them in the chart. Write each word one time.

Mom to the Rescue!

Nick (always) goes home to see his mom once a year. He <u>packs</u> his (gray) <u>bag</u>. What if it (rains)? Nick gets his coat. What if it's hot? Nick gets his swim trunks. He runs to <u>catch</u> the (train), but he forgets his <u>bag</u>! Mom meets Nick in (Bay) City. She <u>asks</u>, "Where is your <u>bag</u>?" <u>At</u> home, Mom looks through the house. Nick (waits). Mom comes <u>back</u> with his old clothes!

9.	always	15.	packs
10.	gray	16.	bag
11.	rains	17.	catch
12.	train	18.	asks
13.	Bay	19.	At
14.	waits	20.	back

Name _____

Multisyllabic Words

A. Read each word. Write how many syllables it has.

1.

weekend

_____2_____

2.

crow

_____1_____

3.

rowboat

_____2_____

4.

train

_____1_____

5.

coast

_____1_____

6.

seashell

_____2_____

7.

sunset

_____2_____

8.

stream

_____1_____

B. Now read the story. Circle the words with two syllables. Write each word in the chart one time. Then write the syllables.

At the (Seashore)

Dean goes to the (seashore) on (weekends.) On

wet days, Dean wears his (raincoat) down to

the beach. He hunts for (seashells) and digs for

clams. On warm days, he stays on a (sailboat)

with his dad. They sail from (sunrise) to (sunset.)

Dean loves his (weekends) at the (seashore)

	Word	Syllables	
9.	seashore	sea	shore
10.	weekends	week	ends
11.	raincoat	rain	coat
12.	seashells	sea	shells
13.	sailboat	sail	boat
14.	sunrise	sun	rise
15.	sunset	sun	set

Name _____

Build Reading Fluency

▶ **Phrasing**

A. When you read, pause between groups of words that go together.

Stay in your seat / while we move through the water. //
This is an important place / for animals, / too. //

B. Listen to the story. When you hear a short pause, write a / . When you
hear a long pause, write //.

Example: Welcome to Black Creek Wetland. // What a great way to spend / a Sunday afternoon. //

Explore a Wetland

Welcome to Black Creek Wetland.//What
a great way to spend/a Sunday afternoon!//
My name/is Jean Clay.//I am your guide.//
Step into the rowboat,//Stay in your seat/
while we move through the water.//

Canada has many wetlands.//Black Creek
Wetland/is one of them.//A wetland is a low,/
wet place.//Rainwater and many streams
or rivers/keep it wet.//Black Creek/is on the

shore of Lake Ontario.//Plants such as reeds/
and cattails grow here.//This is an important
place/for animals,/too.//Ducks and geese/lay
their eggs here/in May.//

Sometimes,/people drain the water/
from wetlands.//Then they use the land/to
grow wheat/or other crops.//Not here.//
We plan to keep this wetland/for the ducks,/
geese,/and other animals.//

C. Now read the story to a partner. Read groups of words together. Make a
short pause when you see a /. Make a long pause when you see a // .

Language and Literacy

Name _____

Special Places, Special People

▶ **Capitalization: Proper Nouns**

A. A proper noun names one particular person, place, or thing.

A proper noun begins with a <u>capital</u> letter.

name of a person	**<u>S</u>abrina** helps kids at a summer camp.
name of a special place, a city, or a country	She works at **<u>C</u>amp <u>B</u>ellwood** in **<u>C</u>loverdale**, **<u>N</u>ew <u>Y</u>ork**.
name of a month or a day	Camp begins on **<u>S</u>aturday**, **<u>J</u>une** 30.

B. Read each sentence. Circle the letters that should be capital letters.

1. Camp (b)ellwood is in (c)loverdale, New York.

2. It is near (s)utter (m)ountain.

3. Many campers come from (b)oston, (m)assachusetts.

4. They learn to swim at (l)ake (b)ronson.

5. Their teacher is (m)indy (l)ee.

6. Sabrina and (j)amal take campers on a hike through the forest.

7. There is a big party at camp on (t)hursday, (j)uly 4.

8. On Wednesday, (j)uly 10, the campers visit Joe (t)aylor at his farm.

9. The next week, Jamal takes them to (n)iagara Falls.

10. Everyone is sorry when camp ends on (f)riday, (a)ugust 2.

Learn Key Vocabulary

The Water Planet: Key Vocabulary

A. Study each word. Circle a number to rate how well you know it. Then complete the chart.

Rating Scale	**1** I have never seen this word before.	**2** I am not sure of the word's meaning.	**3** I know this word and can teach the word's meaning to someone else.

▲ The **world's surface** is covered by **oceans**.

Key Words	Check Understanding	Deepen Understanding
❶ cold (cōld) *adjective* Rating: 1 2 3	Ice and snow are **cold**. (Yes) No	What happens when you are in a cold place? *Responses will vary. Possible responses could refer to people shivering or seeing their breath.*
❷ ocean (ō-shun) *noun* Rating: 1 2 3	An **ocean** is smaller than a pond. Yes (No)	What would you find in the ocean? *Responses will vary. Possible responses could mention big waves, whales, lots of fish, or seaweed.*
❸ surface (sur-fes) *noun* Rating: 1 2 3	Lakes are on Earth's **surface**. (Yes) No	Describe Earth's surface in our region. *Responses will vary. Possible responses could relate to hills, flat lands, or lakes in the area.*

Name _____

The **ocean** near this beach is **warm**. ▶

Key Words	Check Understanding	Deepen Understanding
❹ warm (wôrm) *adjective* Rating: 1 2 3	Things freeze in **warm** places. Yes (No)	Name two warm places *Responses will vary but should refer to locations, states, or countries that are usually warm.* _____ _____ _____
❺ world (wirld) *noun* Rating: 1 2 3	Our **world** has both land and water. (Yes) No	What part of the world do you live in? *Responses will vary. Possible responses could relate to the nation, continent, or hemisphere.* _____ _____ _____

B. Use at least two of the Key Vocabulary words. Tell how you use water every day.

Answers will vary.

_____

_____

_____

Name _____

Plan and Write

1. What place would you like to write about? _____

2. Look for ideas in books, magazines, or on the Internet. Fill in a concept map.

_____   _____

_____   (How to   )   (What to see)   _____
                         (get there)
_____   _____

                              (Place)

                              _____

3. Write a title.
                                        _____

4. Write about a place.
   - Use commands.   Take _____.
   - Use adjectives.
   - Tell how to get there.   Explore _____.

                           You can _____.

                           _____

                           _____

                           _____

                           _____

5. Copy your sentences onto cards. Attach the cards to a large piece of paper. Add pictures.

Check Your Work

▶ Capitalization and Plurals

Read the travel guide. Fix capital letters and plural nouns as needed.
Mark your changes. Then write the paragraph correctly.

Visit Florida Now!

Take a trip to sunny Florida! You can learn about space travel at the ̲k̲ennedy Space Center.
You can swim at the white sand beaches in f̲ort m̲yers. You can ride on fun rides at d̲isney
world. You can see many alligator^s in the Everglades. Explore f̲lorida! There is so much to
see and do!

Take a trip to sunny Florida! You can learn about space travel at the Kennedy Space Center. You can swim

at the white sand beaches in Fort Myers. You can ride on fun rides at Disney World. You can see many

alligators in the Everglades. Explore Florida! There is so much to see and do!

Mind Map

Use the mind map to show ideas about friends and friendship. As you read the selections in this unit, add new ideas you learn about what friends do together.

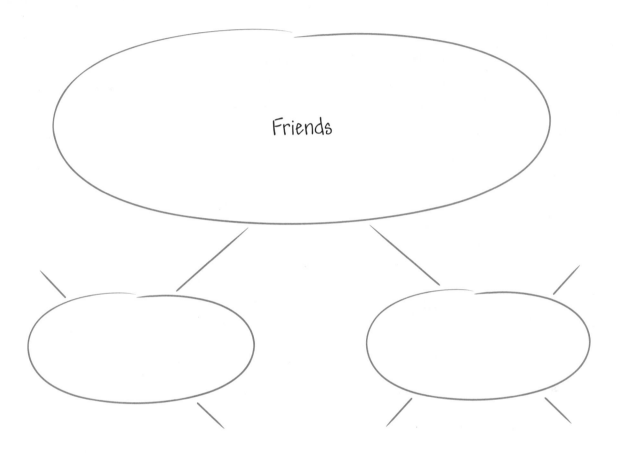

Friends

Language Development

Name _____

They Cooked Pizza Together

▶ **Language: Describe Actions**

▶ **Grammar: Past Tense Verbs**

Complete each sentence. Tell what the friends did.
Use a verb from the box.

laughed	helped	spilled	rolled
enjoyed	looked	cooked	watched

1.

Miguel ____rolled____ the dough.

Len ____looked____ at the cookbook.

2.

Miguel ____spilled____ sauce.

Len ____laughed____ about the mess.

3.

Then Len ____helped____ with the dough.

Miguel ____watched____ him.

4.

Finally, the boys ____cooked____ the pizza.

They ____enjoyed____ their dinner.

Name _____

How Do They Feel?

▶ **Vocabulary: Feelings**

▶ **Language: Express Feelings**

A. Look at each picture. Tell how the person feels. Use a word from the box.

scared	confused	bored	mad	proud	sad

1.

_____confused_____

2.

_____bored_____

3.

_____mad_____

4.

_____scared_____

5.

_____sad_____

6.

_____proud_____

B. Read each sentence. Tell how you feel.

Answers will vary. Accept reasonable responses.

7. I get a good grade on my test.

   I feel __proud__ .

8. My best friend moves to another city.

   I am __sad__ .

9. There is nothing for me to do.

   I feel __bored__ .

10. A bee buzzes around my head.

    I am __scared__ .

It Was Fun to Study Together

▶ **Grammar: Irregular Past Tense Verbs: *Was* and *Were***

Use *was* and *were* to tell about the past.

Pronoun	Verb	Example
I	was	I **was** in the library.
you	were	You **were** by the bookshelf.
he, she, it	was	It **was** warm in the library.
we	were	We **were** not bored.
they	were	They **were** curious about the magazines.

Use **There was** for one person or thing.
Use **There were** for two or more.

There was a girl beside me.
There were many books to read.

Complete each sentence. Use *was* or *were*.

1. It _____was_____ 1:30.

2. I _____was_____ with my friends.

3. We _____were_____ in the library.

4. Other students _____were_____ there, too.

5. There _____was_____ a new librarian at the desk.

6. Our table _____was_____ not very big.

7. Carol _____was_____ beside me.

8. There _____were_____ good magazines on the shelf.

9. Mr. Smith _____was_____ glad to answer my questions.

10. It _____was_____ fun to study with my friends.

Name _____

We Weren't There!

▶ Grammar: Negative Sentences and Contractions with *Not*

There are different ways to build negative sentences in the past tense.

Add the word **not** after **was** and **were**.

She **was not** happy.

We **were not** on time.

With other verbs, add **did not** <u>before</u> the verb.

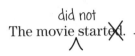

The movie started̶.

did not
∧

> **When you add *did not* to a sentence, take the *-ed* off the main verb.**

Complete the sentence. Use *did not, was not,* or *were not*.
Then rewrite the sentence. Use a contraction.

> **Contractions**
>
> did + not = didn't
>
> was + not = wasn't
>
> were + not = weren't

1. Kelli ____was not____ late.

   ___Kelli wasn't late.___

2. Dina and I ____were not____ there.

   ___Dina and I weren't there.___

3. We ____did not____ answer the phone.

   ___We didn't answer the phone.___

4. The bus ____did not____ stop for us.

   ___The bus didn't stop for us.___

5. We ____were not____ on time for the movie.

   ___We weren't on time for the movie.___

6. Kelli ____was not____ happy.

   ___Kelli wasn't happy.___

Identify Causes and Effects

▶ **Sum It Up**

A. Read the passage. Look for causes and effects. Complete the cause-and-effect chart.

> ### The New Kid
>
> Luis felt nervous as he walked into the lunch room. This was his first day at Greenfield Middle School. He didn't know anyone, so he sat at table by himself.
>
> "How will I ever make friends?" he wondered. "All these people already know each other. They've been in school together for two months." Someone settling into the seat beside him interrupted Luis's thoughts.
>
> "Hi, I'm Eduardo," said the boy. "I just started in this school last week, and I don't know anyone." Suddenly, Luis felt much better. He thought Eduardo might be his first new friend at his new school.

Answers will vary. Sample responses are given.

Cause-and-Effect Chart

Causes	Effects
It was Luis's first day at a new school.	Luis felt nervous.
He didn't know anyone.	He sat by himself.
Eduardo didn't know anyone either.	Eduardo sat with Luis.
Luis thought Eduardo might be his friend.	Luis felt better.

B. Write a sentence for each cause and effect in the chart. Use the word *because*.

1. Luis felt nervous because it was his first day at a new school.

2. He sat by himself because he didn't know anyone.

3. Eduardo sat with Luis because he didn't know anyone either.

4. Luis felt better because he thought Eduardo might be his friend.

Language and Literacy

High Frequency Words, Part 1

A. Read each word. Then write it.

1. saw _____ saw _____

2. was _____ was _____

3. were _____ were _____

4. their _____ their _____

5. said _____ said _____

B. Write the answer to each question. Find the new words in the box. Write the words on the lines.

6. Which 2 words have 3 letters?

_____ saw _____   _____ was _____

7. Which word rhymes with **her**?

_____ were _____

8. Which word has 5 letters?

_____ their _____

9. Which word rhymes with **red**?

_____ said _____

10. Which word is the past tense of **see**?

_____ saw _____

Name _____

High Frequency Words, Part 2

A. Read each word. Then write it.

1. began _____began_____

2. about _____about_____

3. dance _____dance_____

4. thought _____thought_____

5. again _____again_____

B. Write the answer to each question. Find the new words in the box. Write the words on the lines.

6. Which word means "started"?

_____began_____

7. Which word has 7 letters?

_____thought_____

8. Which 3 words have 2 syllables?

_____began_____   _____about_____   _____again_____

9. Which 4 words have 5 letters each?

_____began_____   _____dance_____

_____about_____   _____again_____

10. Which word means "once more"?

_____again_____

Language and Literacy

Verbs with -ed

A. Read each sentence. Change the word in dark type to tell about the past.

1. Lin and I ___planted___ seeds.
   (plant)

2. The next day it ___rained___ on our seeds.
   (rain)

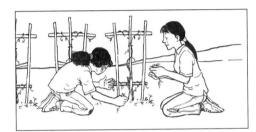

3. I ___helped___ her pull the weeds.
   (help)

4. We ___waited___ for the plants to grow.
   (wait)

5. We ___picked___ a lot of peas.
   (pick)

6. We ___cooked___ them for our friends.
   (cook)

B. Now read the story. Circle the words with -ed. Write each word in the chart one time. Then write the root word.

We (Waited) for the Sun

On Saturday morning it (rained). Kim and I (waited) for the sun. When it (peeked) through the clouds, we ran to the beach. We saw some birds and (hunted) for shells by the water. We (cleaned) the sand off the shells and put them in a box. Then we (hunted) for tiny crabs in the sand. Kim (lifted) one crab so we could see it up close.

Word with -ed	Root Word
7. Waited	wait
8. rained	rain
9. peeked	peek
10. hunted	hunt
11. cleaned	clean
12. lifted	lift

Verbs with -*ed*

A. Read each sentence. Change the word in dark type to tell about the past.

1. Lane and I ____planned____ a trip.
   (plan)

2. We ____grabbed____ some snacks and water.
   (grab)

3. We ____hiked____ in the hills for six hours.
   (hike)

4. We laughed and ____joked____ the whole time.
   (joke)

5. We ____stopped____ just before dark.
   (stop)

6. Later, we ____bragged____ to another friend about the trip.
   (brag)

B. Now read the story. Circle the words with -*ed*. Write each word in the chart one time. Then write the root word.

With a Friend

Ben's feet (dragged) as he (jogged) in the park.

Sometimes he (hated) to jog by himself. He sat

down on a bench to rest. Just then his friend

Matt (jogged) by and (waved.)

"Matt!" Ben said. "Wait for me!" He (hopped)

up and ran to catch up with Matt. He (smiled)

as they ran side by side. It was more fun to jog

with a friend!

	Word with -*ed*	Root Word
7.	dragged	drag
8.	jogged	jog
9.	hated	hate
10.	waved	wave
11.	hopped	hop
12.	smiled	smile

Build Reading Fluency

▶ Phrasing

A. When you read, pause between groups of words that go together.

She looked at the clock / above the stove. //
"Veronica has ten more seconds to get
here," / she said. //

B. Listen to the story. When you hear a short pause, write a / .
When you hear a long pause, write //.

Example: Eva was mad. //She tapped her foot. // She looked at the clock / above the stove. //

Eva's Lesson

Eva was mad.//She tapped her foot.//

She looked at the clock/above the stove. //

"Veronica has ten more seconds to get here,"/

she said.//Eva waited and waited.//Veronica

was always late.//

They had planned/to talk about their dance/

for the school show.//Eva thought Veronica

was not very good.//She thought Veronica

needed a lot of help.//

While she waited,/Eva played the CD for

their dance.//She clapped her hands/and

kicked to the beat.//She began to sing.//She

kicked again.//This time,/she kicked too high.//

She slipped/and landed on the rug.//Just then,/

Veronica peeked in the kitchen window.//She

saw Eva/and rushed to help her.//Eva smiled/

and rubbed her leg./"I thought you were the

one who needed help. Now I know/I/was the

one,"/she joked.//

C. Now read the story to a partner. Read groups of words together. Make a
short pause when you see a /. Make a long pause when you see //.

Meg's Friends

▶ **Possessive Nouns**

A. Some nouns show ownership. They end in 's.

Meg's best friend is Helen. Helen's family lives next door. Helen has a brother. Her brother's name is Fred.

B. Complete each sentence. Add 's to the word in dark print.

1. ____Meg's____ favorite sport is tennis.
   (Meg)

2. Her ____friend's____ favorite game is tennis, too.
   (friend)

3. Meg uses her ____dad's____ racket to play tennis.
   (dad)

4. Helen borrows her ____brother's____ racket.
   (brother)

5. ____Fred's____ racket is new.
   (Fred)

6. ____Helen's____ mom and dad take the girls
   (Helen)
   to the park.

7. They play tennis in the ____city's____ park.
   (city)

8. Then ____Helen's____ brother brings the girls home.
   (Helen)

This player is shouting because he is **angry** about how the game is going. ▶

Hand in Hand: Key Vocabulary

A. Study each word. Circle a number to rate how well you know it. Then complete the chart.

Rating Scale	**1** I have never seen this word before.	**2** I am not sure of the word's meaning.	**3** I know this word and can teach the word's meaning to someone else.

Key Words	Check Understanding	Deepen Understanding
❶ **angry** (**āng**-rē) *adjective* **Rating:** 1 2 3	When you feel **angry**, you are mad about something. (Yes) No	How do you help yourself feel better after you get angry? *Responses will vary. Possible responses could refer to taking a deep breath, going for a walk, or talking to a friend.*
❷ **different** (**di**-fur-rent) *adjective* **Rating:** 1 2 3	Friends can have **different** ideas and still like each other. (Yes) No	Name two different languages. *Responses will vary but should identify real languages.*
❸ **friendship** (**frend**-ship) *noun* **Rating:** 1 2 3	**Friendship** develops when people like each other. (Yes) No	Name one important thing in a friendship. *Responses will vary. Possible responses could relate to trusting each other, sharing interests, or doing things together.*

Name _____

▲ This **group** is made of many **different** people who are all friends.

Key Words	Check Understanding	Deepen Understanding
❹ group (groop) *noun* **Rating:** 1 2 3	You can play music in more than one **group**. (Yes) No	Describe a group that you belong to. *Responses will vary. Possible responses could relate to school classes, teams, or family groups.* _____ _____ _____
❺ hoped (hōpt) *verb* **Rating:** 1 2 3	Many people have **hoped** for world peace. (Yes) No	Describe something you have hoped for. *Responses will vary. Possible responses could relate to things students would like to have or more abstract ideas, such as peace.* _____ _____ _____

B. Use at least two of the Key Vocabulary words. Tell about a time when you learned something from someone from a different group.

Answers will vary.

_____

_____

_____

Name _____

Plan and Write

1. Think about a time when you did something fun with a friend. What did you do? Where did you do it? How did you feel? Use the chart to answer the questions.

What We Did	Where	My Feelings

2. Write a title.

3. Tell the **names** of your friends in the first sentence.

4. Tell what you did. Use the **past tense**. Tell how you felt. Use **feeling words**.

_____

_____

_____

_____

_____

_____

_____

_____

Check Your Work

▶ Capitalization and Focus

Read the memory story. Fix capital letters as needed. Take out any sentences that are not about the memory. Mark your changes. Then write the story correctly.

A Green Day with Kwami

by Declan O'Carroll

One day Kwami asked me to lunch at his house. Mrs. jones cooked a special meal. I was surprised when i saw the plate. It had green mashed potatoes, green beans, and green eggs! My sister Zeena is a good cook. We ate the green food. It looked funny but tasted good! Then kwami and i went downtown to the St. patrick's Day parade. Everyone wore green. It was a green day!

One day Kwami asked me to lunch at his house. Mrs. Jones cooked a special meal. I was surprised when

I saw the plate. It had green mashed potatoes, green beans, and green eggs! We ate the green food. It looked

funny but tasted good! Then Kwami and I went downtown to the St. Patrick's Day parade. Everyone wore green.

It was a green day!

Mind Map

Use the mind map to show how people celebrate. As you read the selections in this unit, add new ideas you learn about the ways people celebrate around the world.

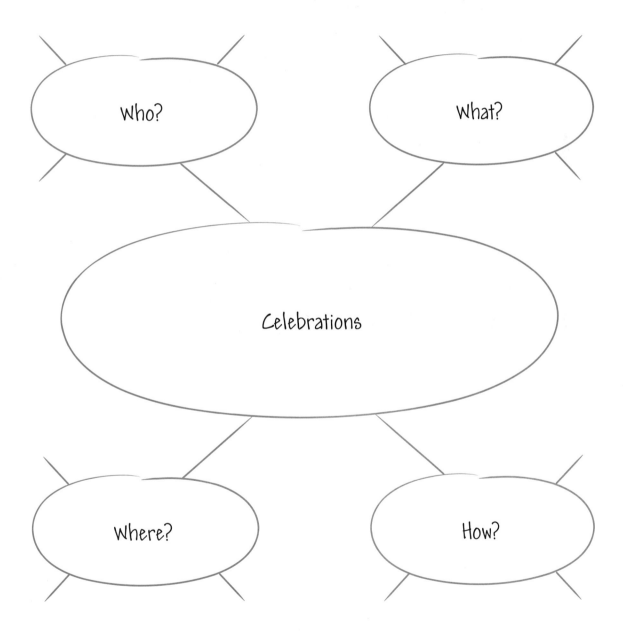

Language Development

How Does He Dance?

Answers will vary. Accept reasonable responses.

▶ **Language: Ask and Answer Questions**

▶ **Grammar: Adverbs**

Look at each picture. Answer the question. Use an adverb from the box.

up	back	high	slowly	forward	now

1.

Where does Matt stretch?

Matt stretches _____up_____ .

2.

Where does Matt reach?

He reaches _____forward_____ .

3.

How does Matt bend?

Matt bends _____slowly / forward_____ .

4.

Can Matt go back?

No, Matt can't go _____back_____ .

5.

Can Matt jump?

Yes, Matt can jump _____high / up_____ .

6.

When can he dance?

He can dance _____now_____ .

What Are They Doing?

▶ **Grammar: Present Progressive Verbs**

These verbs tell what is happening now.

The girls **are celebrating** their culture.
They **are standing** in line.
The powwow **is starting** soon.

Complete each sentence. Tell what the people are doing. Use verbs from the box.

are moving	is stepping	are enjoying	are playing
is singing	are sitting	is hopping	is listening

1. The dancer _____is stepping_____ quickly.

2. His feet _____are moving_____ forward.

3. He _____is hopping_____ up and down.

4. He _____is listening / stepping_____ to the music.

Answers will vary. Accept reasonable responses.

5. The children _____are sitting_____ in a circle.

6. They _____are playing_____ the drums.

7. One boy _____is singing_____ a song.

8. The children _____are enjoying / playing_____ the music.

Language Development

Name _____

Dancers Around the World

▶ **Vocabulary: Country Words**

▶ **Language: Describe People**

A. Look at each picture. Complete the sentences. Use words from the box.

Scotland	Scottish	Cambodia	Cambodian

1.

Scotland
Ireland
England

2.

Laos
Thailand   Vietnam
Cambodia

This dancer is from _____Scotland_____ .

She is _____Scottish_____ .

These dancers are _____Cambodian_____ .

They are doing a dance from
_____Cambodia_____ .

B. Describe the dancers. Tell what they look like. Tell what they are doing.
Complete the sentences.

Answers will vary. Sample responses are given.

3. The Scottish dancer is from ___Scotland_____ .

4. She wears a ___white shirt_____ .

5. The dancer is ___turning_____ .

6. The ___Cambodian_____ dancers are sitting.

7. They have ___tall hats_____ .

8. These dancers are ___telling a story with their hands_____ .

142   Unit 9 Let's Celebrate!   © NGSP & HB

We Like to Dance!

▶ Grammar: Phrases with *Like To* and *Want To*

Use a verb to complete a phrase with *like to* or *want to*.

| like to | + | verb |

They **like to dance** together.

She **likes to step** to the music.

| want to | + | verb |

They **want to learn** more steps.

He **wants to teach** people.

Add an -s when you use he, she, or it.

Complete the sentences for each picture. Use *like to* or *want to*.   *Answers will vary. Sample responses are given.*

1.

The students _____like to_____ leap.

They _____want to_____ perform for the

Russian ballet.

2.

The boy _____wants to_____ spin.

He _____likes to_____ dance fast.

3.

The boys _____want to_____ celebrate
the Chinese New Year.

They _____like to_____ carry the
dragon costume.

4.

The dancer from India _____wants to_____
share a story.

She _____likes to_____ show it with
her dance.

Name _____

Classify Information

▶ **Sum It Up**

A. Think about the kind of dancing you like to do. Fill in the concept map. Tell who you dance with, why you dance, where you dance, and how you dance.

Answers will vary. Sample responses are given.

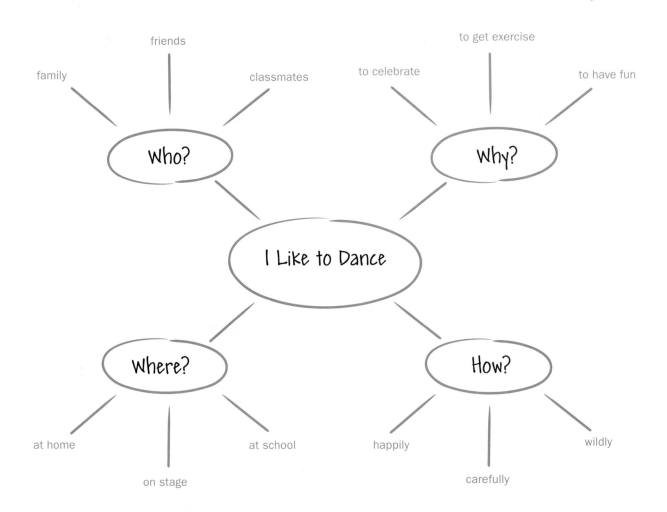

B. Write sentences to tell about the way you like to dance. Use words from your concept map in your sentences.

Answers will vary. Sentences should be based on information classsified in the concept map.

_____

_____

_____

_____

Language and Literacy

High Frequency Words, Part 1

A. Read each word. Then write it.

1. celebrate _____celebrate_____

2. most _____most_____

3. young _____young_____

4. children _____children_____

5. started _____started_____

B. Write the answer to each question. Find the new words in the box. Write the words on the lines.

6. This word ends in **e**.

    _____celebrate_____

7. These 2 words have **st**.

    _____most_____   _____started_____

8. This word is the opposite of **old**.

    _____young_____

9. This word begins with **ch**.

    _____children_____

10. This word is the opposite of **ended**.

    _____started_____

Language and Literacy

High Frequency Words, Part 2

A. Read each word. Then write it.

1. beginning _____ beginning _____

2. change _____ change _____

3. another _____ another _____

4. only _____ only _____

5. following _____ following _____

B. Read each sentence. Find the new words in the box. Write the words on the lines.

6. These 2 words end with **ing**.

_____ following _____   _____ beginning _____

7. This word ends with **e**.

_____ change _____

8. This word has the word **other** in it.

_____ another _____

9. Which word has 4 letters?

_____ only _____

10. This word starts with **f**.

_____ following _____

Language and Literacy

Verbs with *-ing*

A. Read each sentence. Change the word in dark type to tell what is happening right now.

1. They are ____celebrating____ summer.
   (celebrate)

2. Some people are ____taking____ trips.
   (take)

3. They are ____swimming____ in the pool.
   (swim)

4. They are ____getting____ wet.
   (get)

5. This family is ____sitting____ outside.
   (sit)

6. They are ____eating____ a picnic lunch.
   (eat)

B. Now read the story. Circle the words with *-ing*. Write each word in the chart one time. Then write the root word.

Our School Fair

Our school fair is (beginning) at 2 p.m. We are (taking) all the games outside. Suddenly, it is (raining) and we are (beginning) to get very wet. Most of us are (rushing) inside. Now we are (waiting) for the rain to stop. Yes. The sun is (shining) again. The fair can begin on time.

Word with *-ing*	Root Word
7. beginning	begin
8. taking	take
9. raining	rain
10. rushing	rush
11. waiting	wait
12. shining	shine

Build Reading Fluency

▶ Phrasing

A. When you read, pause between groups of words that go together.

They are greeting / the Chinese dragon, / which brings good luck. //
People dance / to celebrate an important day / in the family. //

B. Listen to the story. When you hear a short pause, write a / .
When you hear a long pause, write //.

Example: This bride / is having fun at her wedding. //

Dance to Celebrate

People dance to celebrate a holiday.//These people/are beginning the Chinese

New Year with a dance.//They are greeting/the Chinese dragon,/which brings

good luck.//Nine men inside the costume/are lifting the dragon/with long poles.//

Only one man is beating a drum.//He is following the dragon.//

People dance/to celebrate an important day/in the family.//This bride/is

having fun at her wedding.//Three young men/are lifting her/in her seat/while

her husband watches.//The family is dancing around them.//They are smiling/and

clapping.//

C. Now read the story to a partner. Read groups of words together. Make a
short pause when you see a /. Make a long pause when you see a //.

Kite Festival: Key Vocabulary

A. Study each word. Circle a number to rate how well you know it. Then complete the chart.

Rating Scale	**1** I have never seen this word before.	**2** I am not sure of the word's meaning.	**3** I know this word and can teach the word's meaning to someone else.

▲ **Colorful** kites fly **gracefully** through the air.

Key Words	Check Understanding	Deepen Understanding
❶ celebrate (**se**-luh-brāt) *verb* Rating: 1 2 3	Americans **celebrate** the Fourth of July. (Yes) No	How do you celebrate a birthday? *Responses will vary but should relate to things people do on birthdays.*
❷ colorful (**cul**-er-ful) *adjective* Rating: 1 2 3	Gray skies are **colorful**. Yes (No)	Which of your clothes are colorful? *Responses will vary. Possible responses include hats, shirts, costumes, or scarves.*
❸ enjoy (en-**joi**) *verb* Rating: 1 2 3	Most people **enjoy** holidays. (Yes) No	Tell what you enjoy about one holiday. *Responses will vary but should relate to enjoyable things people do on holidays.*

Name _____

Teams **celebrate** the kite festival by flying a **colorful** kite. ▶

Key Words	Check Understanding	Deepen Understanding
❹ gracefully (grās-ful-lē) *adverb* Rating: 1 2 3	Ballet dancers move **gracefully**. (Yes) No	Describe something that moves gracefully. *Responses will vary. Possible responses could include fish swimming, people dancing, or people skiing.* _____ _____ _____
❺ started (stär-ted) *verb* Rating: 1 2 3	The day has not **started** yet. Yes (No)	Describe how one of your family parties started. *Responses will vary. Possible responses could relate to people arriving or food being put out.* _____ _____ _____

B. Use at least two of the Key Vocabulary words. Describe what it would be like to watch the kite festival in Japan.

Answers will vary.

_____

_____

_____

Name _____

Plan and Write

1. Choose a celebration. _____

2. What do you want to write about? Make a list of questions.

   A. How _____

   B. Where _____

   C. What _____

3. Use your questions to interview someone about the celebration. Write the answers.

   A. _____

   B. _____

   C. _____

4. Write a title.

5. Name the **celebration** and the **country** in the first sentence.

6. Write sentences. Tell what people **like to** do at the celebration.

_____

_____

_____

_____

_____

_____

_____

_____

_____

_____

_____

_____

Name _____

Check Your Work

▶ Capitalization and Details

Read the blog. Fix capital letters where they are needed. Take out any detail that does not go with the topic. Mark your changes. Then write the blog correctly.

Mark Your Changes
≡ Capitalize.
ℛ Take out.

Chinese Lunar New Year

Many people from china celebrate the Lunar New Year. we go to parades where people dress like lions and dragons. There are similar celebrations for the new year in other countries like vietnam. ~~We also go to parades on memorial day and the fourth of July.~~ this celebration is also special because families get together for a reunion dinner and eat special food. Chinese Lunar New Year is celebrated in different months. Sometimes it falls in january. Sometimes it is in february.

Many people from China celebrate the Lunar new year. We go to parades where people dress like lions and dragons. There are similar celebrations for the new year in other countries like Vietnam. This celebration is also special because families get together for a reunion dinner and eat special food. Chinese Lunar new year is celebrated in different months. Sometimes it falls in January. Sometimes it is in February.

_____

_____

_____

_____

_____

_____

_____

_____

Timed Reading Chart

How many words did you read correctly for each
selection? Complete the chart to show your scores
for each day.

Name _____

*Results will vary. Help students as necessary to record their
reading scores from each selection on the chart by filling in
the appropriate number of squares. Meet periodically with
each student to discuss the chart and individual results.*

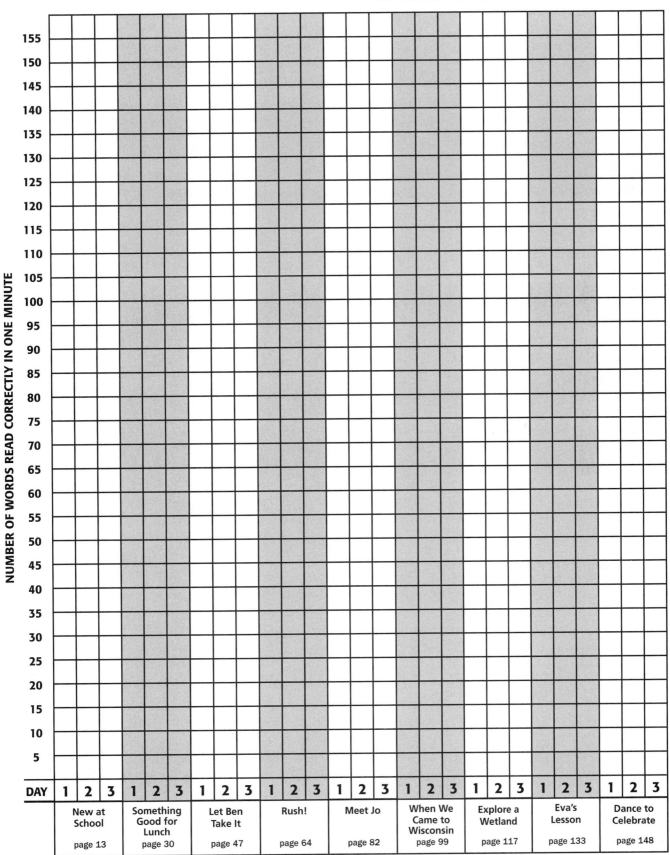

NUMBER OF WORDS READ CORRECTLY IN ONE MINUTE

155, 150, 145, 140, 135, 130, 125, 120, 115, 110, 105, 100, 95, 90, 85, 80, 75, 70, 65, 60, 55, 50, 45, 40, 35, 30, 25, 20, 15, 10, 5

DAY	1	2	3	1	2	3	1	2	3	1	2	3	1	2	3	1	2	3	1	2	3	1	2	3	1	2	3

New at School	Something Good for Lunch	Let Ben Take It	Rush!	Meet Jo	When We Came to Wisconsin	Explore a Wetland	Eva's Lesson	Dance to Celebrate
page 13	page 30	page 47	page 64	page 82	page 99	page 117	page 133	page 148

Decodable Stories

Contents

A Bad Day!

This is not a good day!

Words with /ă/a; /ŏ/o

am	class	lot	tan
and	dad	mad	van
at	ham	mom	
bad	has	not	
bag	hot	sad	
can	jog	stops	

High Frequency Words for Unit 1

home

Unit 1 Glad to Meet You!

I am at school at 8:00.

I am at lunch at 12:00.
I have hot ham. I do not like
ham. I am sad and mad.

I have a class at 8:15. I do not have my tan bag. My tan bag is at home.

I jog a lot in P.E. I am hot! I stop.

Mom is mad. Mom can not come. Dad can.

Dad stops the van. Dad has my tan bag.

Pop!

It is such a mess! Mom does not like it a bit. Jim just grins.

Catch, Mom!

Words with /i/i; /u/u; /ch/ch, tch

bag	fills	it	stuff
big	grabs	Jim	such
bit	grins	just	switch
bunch	hits	much	will
but	hunts	pop	
catch	in	rip	
fast	is	snack	

High Frequency Words for Units 1–2

open	then	there

Unit 2 Set the Table

Jim hits the TV switch.

Popcorn fills the room fast!

Oh, no!

3

Then Jim hunts for a snack. There is just a bunch of old stuff, but Jim does spot a bag of . . . .

Jim looks at his snack. Jim can spot a rip in the bag. Jim opens the microwave.

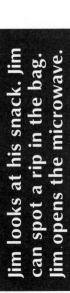

Jim grabs a bag. He does not spot a rip in the bag.

It will not take much time.

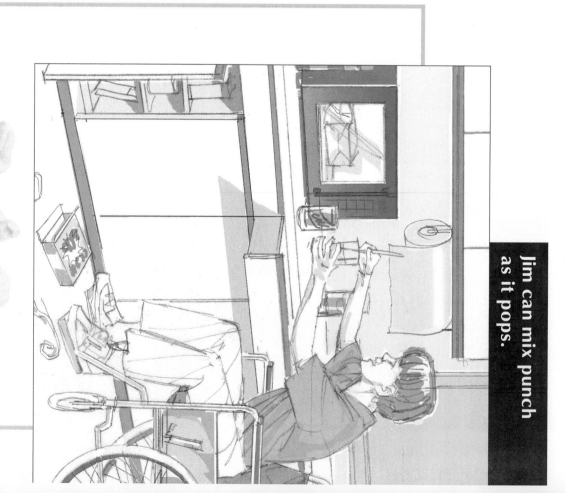

Jim can mix punch as it pops.

Short e, sh, ck, and Double Consonants

Fred at Work

At last, the day ends. Mom has one last job for Fred.

Fred! Help me carry these bags.

Where is Fred? He is in bed! Zzzzzzz.

Zzzzzzzz

Words with /ĕ/ĕ/; /sh/sh; /k/ck

bed	Fred	mess	stack
chest	fresh	net	trash
docks	gets	picks	when
ends	help	shop	yes

High Frequency Words for Units 1–3

| love | there | want |

Unit 3 On the Job

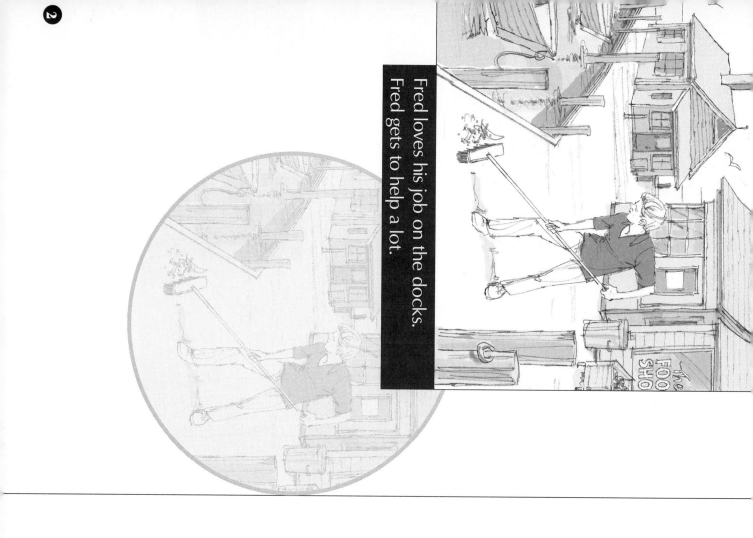

Fred loves his job on the docks.
Fred gets to help a lot.

Fred takes trash to a bin.

THE LUNCH SPOT

4

Jill has a batch of fresh fish.

I can help. I will fill the chest with ice.

Fred helps a girl get her hat.

I get a net for jobs like this.

From Last to First

That day, Fran runs at a track meet. But Fran is not last. Fran is first!

Words with Blends and Digraphs

bang	from	ring	thinks
catch	kids	rush	track
check	last	sock	which
clock	left	spot	
fast	lunch	still	
Fran	pack	that	

High Frequency Words for Units 1–4

first	from	want

Unit 4 Numbers Count

It is 7:00 a.m. on a school day. Fran is still in bed.

Fran! It is 7:00 a.m.!

BANG! BANG!

Fran will not rush.

Fran jumps on the last step. She is the last kid on the bus.

Fran did it!

Good job!

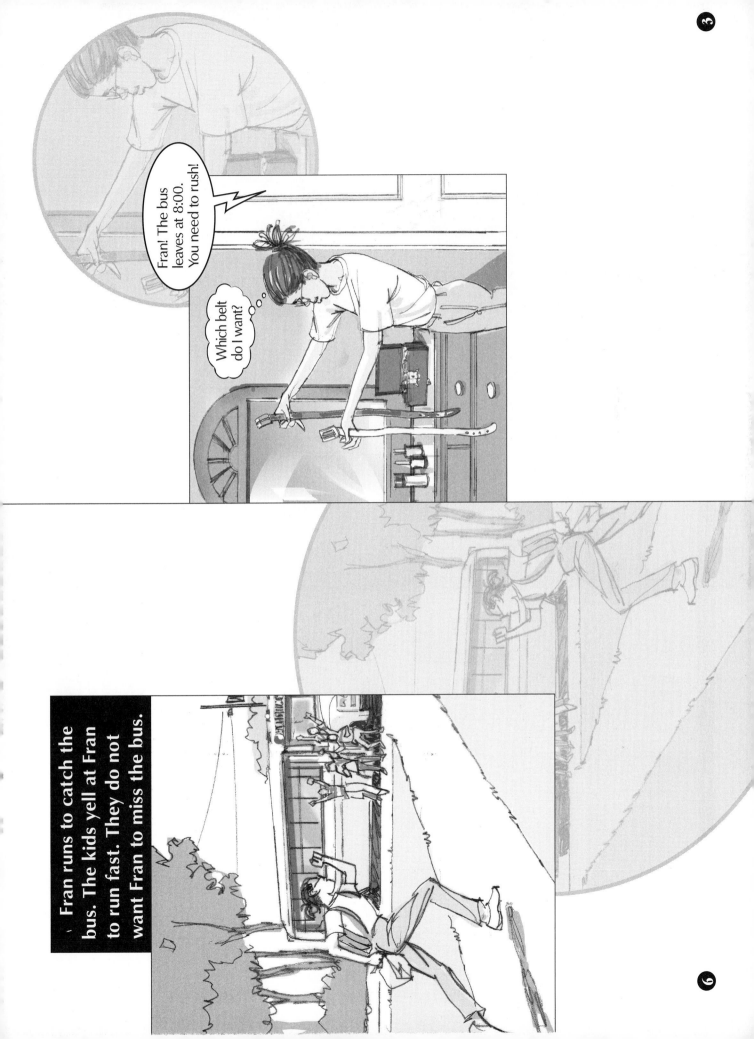

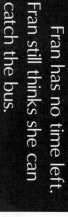

A City Food Festival

Word Patterns and Multisyllabic Words

basket	happens	stand	crab
chips	hundreds	stands	sandwich
chopsticks	is	sum	has
dim	muffins	that	had
Ekram	napkin	this	
festival	Pedro	with	
fish	shish-ke-bob	pumpkin	

High Frequency Words for Units 1–5

all	first	new	something
city	love	next	there
enough	more	people	want
find	move	second	

Unit 5 City Sights

This is Pedro's first time at a food festival.

The boys are still hungry! They see a man with muffins to sell.

At Home

Long Vowels: *a, i, o, u*

Grandmother likes all the things we do for her. She even likes my brother's drums.

BANG!

CRASH!

Words with Long Vowels: *a, i, o, u*

cakes	hope	robe	tune
bake	like	smiles	use
fine	make	take	
home	notes	time	

High Frequency Words for Units 1–6

all	from	out	wants
down	her	together	something
eat	our		

Unit 6 Welcome Home!

© NGSP & HB

My grandmother is here from Japan. Our family is glad to see her. We hope she likes our home.

Soon it is time to eat. We use our best dishes for the food. We take out the best glasses. Then we sit down and eat together. Grandmother smiles and smiles.

I like this food! The cake is good, too!

It smells good!

We want to make Grandmother glad that she came to see us. So we think of special things to do for her. In Japan, Grandmother does not bake cakes. So I make her one.

My mother makes crab rolls for Grandmother.

We really like these. I hope she will, too.

On the River

It's the end of the day.

Well, we don't have any fish.

No, but we had a neat day, and it didn't rain!

Words with Long Vowels: *ai, ay; ee, ea; oa, ow*

cattail	deep	neat	toad
croak	eats	rain	weekend
day	hears	show	year
daytime	near	sleep	

High Frequency Words for Units 1–7

always	place	something	there
animals	river	small	water
one			

In late June, Shane always spends a weekend with his granddad. This year Granddad takes him to Greenstone River. It's a good place to fish. You can also see a lot of wildlife there.

It's almost sunset. Still no fish. Shane asks if fish like this spot.

Granddad knows the best places to find fish.

They wait for the fish to bite. While they wait, Shane sees something.

Look!

That's a bald eagle! It hunts for small animals that live by the water. It eats fish, too.

Shane hears something in the cattail plants.

Look at the toad!

That's a tree frog. Frogs can be hard to spot. They sleep in the daytime.

About Duke

Verb Ending -ed

Hi, Duke! How are you? How is your new home?

Chen, do I need to tell you again? Your dog is just fine!

WOOF!

Words with Verb Ending -ed

hated	jogged	sailed	waited
hunted	played	stepped	

High Frequency Words for Units 1–8

about	animals	really	together
again	love	there	was
always	new	thought	were

Unit 8 Friend to Friend

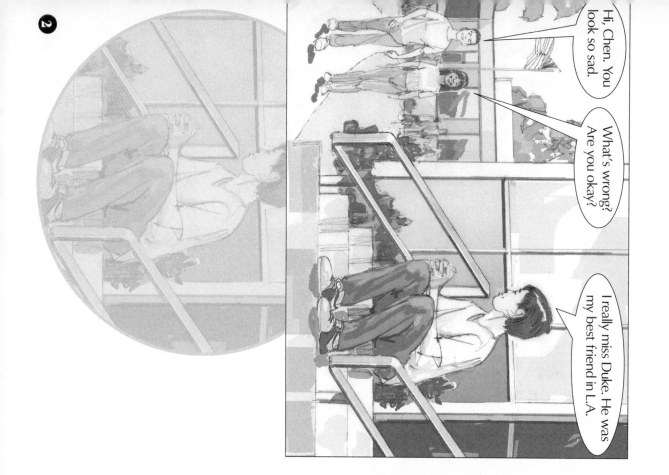

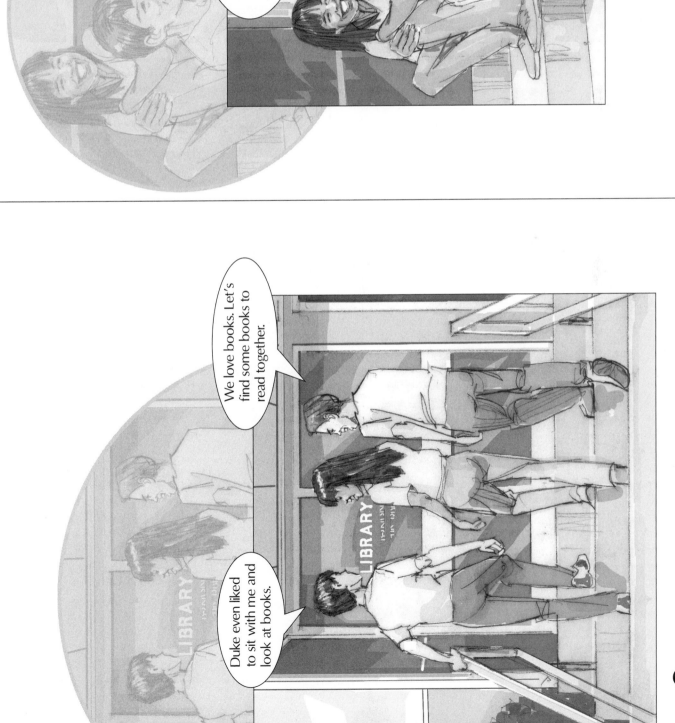

Before I came here, Duke and I were always together. He waited for me after school. He was there to greet me when I stepped off the bus.

We love books. Let's find some books to read together.

Duke even liked to sit with me and look at books.

Celebrate the Past

Children are singing as we leave the fair. I look back, wondering if we really went into the past.

It's fun to celebrate the past this way!

Words with Verb Ending -ing

beginning	joking	singing	thinking
dressing	pinning	slapping	throwing
eating	playing	taking	
getting	scrubbing	tasting	

High Frequency Words for Units 1–9

another	come	really	want
celebrate	people	something	young
city			

Unit 9 Let's Celebrate!

My friends are taking me to a fair. It is like a trip back in time.

This seems like a city in old England.

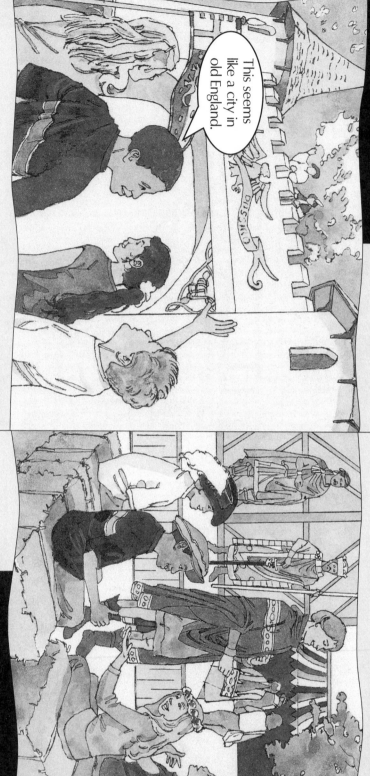

A play is beginning, and the actors are speaking to me! They ask me to come on the stage and be the queen!

People are dressing in costumes. We want to dress up, too. Sam has a velvet cap. Todd is pinning a ribbon on another hat.

We are eating very odd food today. Todd is tasting something called "toad in the hole." I am feasting on "beef on a stick."

They are playing tunes just like people played 400 years ago! A young man is twirling sticks.

Some women are scrubbing clothes in a stream. They are joking and slapping the cloth on rocks.

Photographs

F2 Row 1: (l, lml) Getty Images, (ml) Digital Stock, (rmr, mr) Getty Images, (r) Artville. Row 2: (l) Ryan McVay/Getty Images, (m) Digital Stock, (r) Metaphotos. Row 3: (l) LWA/Getty Images, (m) Harald Sund/Getty Images, (r) Getty Images. Row 4: (l) Steve Cole/Getty Images, (m) Paul Beard/Getty Images, (r) Getty Images. **F3** Row 1: (l, m) Getty Images, (r) Paul Beard/Getty Images. Row 2: (l) Getty Images, (m) EyeWire, (r) Digital Stock. Row 3: (l) Getty Images, (m) Metaphotos, (r) Getty Images. Row 4: (l, m) Digital Stock, (r) Getty Images. Row 5: (l) Artville, (m) Steve Cole/Getty Images, (r) Getty Images. **F4** (tl, tr) Liz Garza Williams, (bl) Digital Stock, (br) Liz Garza Williams. **F5** Row 1: (l, r) Artville: Row 2: (l) Artville, (r) Liz Garza Williams. Row 3: (l, r) Artville. **F6** (t, m) Liz Garza Williams, (b) Artville. **F7** (t, m) Artville, (b) Liz Garza Williams. **F8** Row 1: (l) Artville. Row 2: (l) Getty Images, (r) Liz Garza Williams. Row 3: (l) Artville, (r) Liz Garza Williams. Row 4: (l) Liz Garza Williams, (r) Artville. Row 5: (l, r) Liz Garza Williams. **F9** Row 1: (l) Getty Images, (r) Liz Garza Williams. Row 2: (l) Liz Garza Williams. Row 3: (l) Artville, (r) Liz Garza Williams. Row 4: (l, r) Liz Garza Williams. **F10** Row 1: (l) Image Club, (ml) Janis Christie/Getty Images, (m) Artville, (mr) Liz Garza Williams, (r) John Paul Endress. Row 2: (l) Getty Images, (m) John Paul Endress, (r) Stockbyte. Row 3: (l) John Paul Endress, (m) Artville, (r) Stockbyte. Row 4: (l) Digital Stock, (m) Getty Images, (r) Liz Garza Williams. Row 5: (l) Artville, (m) John Paul Endress, (r) Liz Garza Williams. **F11** Row 1: (l) Artville, (m) D. Falconer/PhotoLink/Getty Images, (r) Getty Images. Row 2: (l) Getty Images, (m) Stockbyte/Getty Images, (r) Liz Garza Williams. Row 3: (l) John Paul Endress, (m) Stockbyte, (r) Liz Garza Williams. Row 4: (l) Liz Garza Williams, (m) Stockbyte, (r) Getty Images. **F15** (t-b) Stockbyte, John Paul Endress, New Century Graphics, Stockbyte/Getty Images. **F16** Row 1: (l) Liz Garza Williams, (r) D. Falconer/PhotoLink/Getty Images. Row 2: (l, r) Liz Garza Williams. Row 3: (l) Stockbyte, (r) John Paul Endress. Row 4: (l, ml) Getty Images, (mr) John Paul Endress, (r) D. Falconer/PhotoLink/Getty Images. Row 5: (l) Artville, (ml, mr, r) Liz Garza Williams, (br) Artville. **F17** Row 1: (l) Artville, (r) Stockbyte. Row 2: (l) Getty Images, (r) John Paul Endress. Row 3: (l) Liz Garza Williams, (r) D. Falconer/PhotoLink/Getty Images. Row 4: (l) Paul Beard/Getty Images, (ml) D. Falconer/PhotoLink/Getty Images, (mr, r) Liz Garza Williams. Row 5: (l) Digital Stock, (ml) Stockbyte, (mr) Getty Images, (r) Liz Garza Williams. Row 6: (l, ml) Liz Garza Williams, (mr) Stockbyte/Getty Images, (r) Liz Garza Williams. **F18** Row 1: (l) Getty Images, (ml) Liz Garza Williams, (m) Getty Images, (mr) Artville, (r) Liz Garza Williams. Row 2: (l) SuperStock, Inc/SuperStock, (ml) John Paul Endress, (mr) Ryan McVay/Getty Images, (r) Image Club. Row 3: (l, ml) Artville, (mr) C Squared Studios/Getty Images, (r) John Paul Endress. Row 4: (l) John Paul Endress, (ml) Stockbyte, (mr) John Paul Endress, (r) Jack Fields/Corbis. Row 5: (l) Artville, (ml) Stockbyte, (mr) EyeWire, (r) Artville. **F19** Row 1: (l) John Paul Endress, (m) Artville, (r) Liz Garza Williams. Row 2: (l) Getty Images, (m) Digital Stock, (r) Stockbyte. Row 3: (l) Laura Dwight/Corbis, (m) Liz Garza Williams, (r) D. Falconer/PhotoLink/Getty Images. Row 4: (l, m) Getty Images, (r) John Paul Endress. **F20**

Liz Garza Williams. **F23** (t-b) Artville, Getty Images, Bill Aron/PhotoEdit, D. Falconer/PhotoLink/Getty Images, Liz Garza Williams. **F24** Row 1: (l) Liz Garza Williams, (m) Stockbyte, (r) Laura Dwight/Corbis. Row 2: (l) Getty Images, (m, r) John Paul Endress. Row 3: (l) Getty Images, (m) D. Falconer/PhotoLink/Getty Images, (r) Getty Images. Row 4: (l) Artville, (m) Thom Lang/Corbis. Row 5: (l, m) Getty Images, (r) Liz Garza Williams. **F25** Row 1: (l) Bill Aron/PhotoEdit, (m) John Paul Endress, (r) Liz Garza Williams. Row 2: (m) Stockbyte, (r) C Squared Studios/Getty Images. Row 3: (l) Laura Dwight/Corbis, (m, r) Artville. Row 4: (l) Laura Dwight/Corbis, (ml) Getty Images, (mr, r) Liz Garza Williams. Row 5: (l) D. Falconer/PhotoLink/Getty Images, (ml) Ryan McVay/Getty Images. Row 6: (l, ml) Getty Images, (mr) C Squared Studios/Getty Images, (r) Stockbyte/Getty Images. **F26** (l, m) Liz Garza Williams. (mr) Getty Images, (r) Digital Studios. **F27** Row 1: (l) Laura Dwight/Corbis, (m) John Paul Endress, (r) Liz Garza Williams. Row 2: (l) Liz Garza Williams, (m) John Paul Endress, (r) Getty Images. Row 3: (l) C Squared Studios/Getty Images, (m) Artville, (r) Charles Krebs/Getty Images. Row 4: (l) Digital Studios, (m) Duomo/Corbis, (r) Liz Garza Williams. **F31** (t) Duomo/Corbis, (m) C Squared Studios/Getty Images, (b) David Young-Wolff/PhotoEdit. **F32** Row 1: (l) C Squared Studios/Getty Images. (ml, mr) Liz Garza Williams, (r) David Young-Wolff/PhotoEdit. Row 2: (l, m) Artville, (r) C Squared Studios/Getty Images. Row 3: (l) John Paul Endress, (m, r) Getty Images. Row 4: (l, ml) Liz Garza Williams, (mr) Artville, (r) David Young-Wolff/PhotoEdit. Row 5: (m, r) Liz Garza Williams. Row 6: (l) D. Falconer/PhotoLink/Getty Images, (m) Ryan McVay/Getty Images, (r) Laura Dwight/Corbis. **F33** Row 1: (l, ml) Liz Garza Williams, (mr) Getty Images, (r) John Paul Endress. Row 2: (l) Getty Images, (m) Bill Aron/PhotoEdit, (r) D. Falconer/PhotoLink/Getty Images. Row 3: (l) Getty Images, (m) Laura Dwight/Corbis, (r) Liz Garza Williams. Row 4: (l) Getty Images, (m) C Squared Studios/Getty Images, (r) Duomo/Corbis. Row 5: (l) Charles Krebs/Getty Images, (m) John Paul Endress, (r) Liz Garza Williams. Row 6: (l) David Young-Wolff/PhotoEdit, (m) Digital Stock, (r) Artville. **F34** (l-ml) John Paul Endress, (m) Image Library, (mr) Artville, (r) John Paul Endress. **F35** Row 1: (l) Liz Garza Williams, (m) Getty Images. Row 2: (l) Roger Ressmeyer/Corbis, (m) New Century Graphics, (r) John Paul Endress. Row 3: (l) Siede Preis/Getty Images, (m) Liz Garza Williams. Row 4: (l) John Paul Endress, (m) Liz Garza Williams, (r) Jack Fields/Corbis. **F39** (t-b) Roger Ressmeyer/Corbis, Liz Garza Williams, Jack Fields/Corbis, Getty Images, Liz Garza Williams, Paul Beard/Getty Images. **F40** Row 1: (l) Getty Images, (r) John Paul Endress, Row 2: (l) Ryan McVay/Getty Images, (m) Liz Garza Williams, (r) Siede Preis/Getty Images. Row 3: (l) Bill Aron/PhotoEdit, (r) Jack Fields/Corbis. Row 4: (l) Liz Garza Williams, (m) Roger Ressmeyer/Corbis, (r) John Paul Endress. Row 5: (l) Liz Garza Williams, (m) Getty Images, (r) D. Falconer/PhotoLink/Getty Images. **F41** Row 1: (m) Bill Aron/PhotoEdit, (r) Stockbyte. Row 2: (l-r) Getty Images. Row 3: (l) Getty Images, (m) C Squared Studios/Getty Images, (r) Getty Images. Row 4: (l) New Century Studios, (ml) Getty Images, (mr) Roger Ressmeyer/Corbis, (r) Artville. Row 5: (l, m) Liz Garza Williams, (r) Siede Preis/Getty Images. Row 6: (l) Liz Garza Williams, (ml) Paul Beard/

Getty Images, (mr) John Paul Endress, (r) Stockbyte. **5** (tl) Image Club, (tr) Liz Garza Williams, (bl) Getty Images, (br) Image Library. **9** Row 1: (l) Liz Garza Williams, (ml) Bill Aron/PhotoEdit, (mr) Laura Dwight/Corbis, (r) Getty Images. Row 2: (l) Liz Garza Williams, (ml, mr) Getty Images, (r) Stockbyte. Row 3: (m) Getty Images, (r) Liz Garza Williams. **10** Row 1: (l) Getty Images, (ml) Burke/Triolo Products/Brand X/Corbis, (mr, r) Getty Images. Row 2 (l) Bill Aron/PhotoEdit, (ml, mr, r) Getty Images. Row 3: (m, r) Getty Images. **11** Row 1: (l) Digital Stock, (ml) Getty Images, (m) John Paul Endress, (mr) Digital Stock. (r) Joel Satore/National Geographic Image Collection. Row 2: (l) William Salaza/Corbis, (ml) Artville, (m, mr) Getty Images, (r) Michael Jan/Getty Images. Row 3: (l) C Squared Studios/Getty Images, (ml) Getty Images, (mr) Digital Stock, (r) Ryan McVay/Getty Images. Row 4: (l) Liz Garza Williams, (m) Artville, (r) Getty Image. **12** Row 1: (l) Artville, (ml) Getty Images, (m) Michael Yamashita/Corbis, (mr, r) Liz Garza Williams. Row 2: (l) Michael Jang/Getty Images. (ml) Bill Aron/PhotoEdit, (m) Getty Images, (mr) Bob Rowan/Corbis, (r) Getty Images. Row 3: (l) Digital Stock, (ml) James Balog/Getty Images, (m) Getty Images, (mr) Artville, (r) Duomo/Corbis. Row 4: (l, ml) Getty Images, (mr) C Squared Studios/Getty Images, (r) Getty Images. Row 5: (l) C Squared Studios/Getty Images, (ml) Burke/Triolo Productions/Brand X/Corbis, (mr) Michael Yamashita/Corbis, (r) Liz Garza Williams. **13** (tl) Liz Garza Williams. **15** (tr) Hola Images/Getty Images. **16** (tr) David Young-Wolff/Getty Images. **20** Row 1: (l) Getty Images, (m) Felisha Martinez/PhotoEdit, (r) Artville. Row 2: (l) Getty Images, (m) Stockbyte. **26** Row 1: (l) D. Falconer/PhotoLink/Getty Images, (ml, mr) Getty Images, (r) Liz Garza Williams. Row 2: (l) Digital Stock, (mr) Getty Images, (r) Liz Garza Williams. Row 3: (m, r) Liz Garza Williams. **27** (l) John Paul Endress, (ml) Liz Garza Williams, (mr) D. Falconer/PhotoLink/Getty Images, (r) Liz Garza Williams. Row 2: (l, ml) Getty Images, (mr) New Century Graphics, (r) Getty Images. Row 3: (m) Getty Images, (r) New Century Graphics. **28** Row 1: (l) John Paul Endress, (ml, m) Getty Images, (mr) Digital Stock, (r) John Paul Endress. Row 2: (l) John Paul Endress, (ml, m) Getty Images, (mr) John Paul Endress, (r) Getty Images. Row 3: (l) D. Falconer/PhotoLink/Getty Images, (ml) James Marshall/Corbis, (m) Getty Images, (mr) Javier Pierini/Getty Images, (r) New Century Graphics. Row 4: (l, ml) Liz Garza Williams, (mr) Alfred Gescheidt/Getty Images, (r) Artville. Row 6: (l) Getty Images, (m) Artville, (r) Getty Images. **29** Row 1: (l) John Paul Endress, (r) Liz Garza Williams. Row 2: (l) Liz Garza Williams. Row 3: (l, r) Liz Garza Williams. Row 4: (l, r) Getty Images, (ml) Liz Garza Williams, (mr) Getty Images, (r) D. Falconer/PhotoLink/Getty Images. Row 5: (l) Stockbyte/Getty Images, (ml) Liz Garza Williams, (mr) John Paul Endress, (r) Liz Garza Williams. Row 6: (l) Getty Images, (ml) John Paul Endress, (mr) Digital Stock, (r) Paul Beard/Getty Images. **30** (tl) Liz Garza Williams. **32** (tr) Getty Images, (m) iStockphoto, (b) Burazin/Getty Images. **33** (tr) StockFood/Getty Images. **37** Row 1: (l) Andrea Pistolesi/Getty Images, (m) Paul Conkllin/PhotoEdit, (r) Liz Garza Williams. Row 2: (l) Ken Fisher/Getty Images, (m) David Young-Wolff/Getty Images, (r) Walter Hodges/Getty Images. **43** Row 1:(l) Digital Studios, (m) John Paul Endress, (r) Steve Cole/Getty Images, Row 2:

(l) Liz Garza Williams, (m) Getty Images, (r) Stockbyte/Getty Images,. Row 3: (l) Charles Krebs/Getty Images, (m) Getty Images, (r) Liz Garza Williams. **44** Row 1: (l) Myrleen Ferguson Cate/PhotoEdit, (ml) David Young-Wolff/PhotoEdit, (mr, r) Artville. Row 2: (l) John Paul Endress, (ml) Louis Grandadam/Getty Images, (mr) LWA-Dann Tardif/Corbis, (r) David Hanover/Getty Images. Row 3: (l, ml) Liz Garza Williams, (mr) John Paul Endress, (r) Michael Newman/PhotoEdit. Row 4: (l) David Frazier/Corbis, (m) Getty Images. **45** Row 1: (l) Getty Images, (ml, mr, r) John Paul Endress. Row 2: (l) Joel Sartore/National Geographic Image Collection, (ml) Eising Food Photography/StockFood, (mr) Peter Correz/Getty Images, (r) EyeWire. Row 3: (l) Robert Bremnel/PhotoEdit, (ml) Bob Elsdale/Getty Images, (mr) Joel Sartore/National Geographic Image Collection, (r) EyeWire. Row 4: (l) Artville, (m) John Paul Endress. **46** Row 1: (l) Liz Garza Williams, (m) Getty Images, (r) Siede Preis/Getty Images. Row 2: (l) Steve Mason/Getty Images, (m) Getty Images, (r) Digital Stock. **47** (tl) Rudi Von Briel/PhotoEdit. **49** (tr) Ken Lucas/Visuals Unlimited. **50** (tr) Richard T. Nowitz/Corbis. **52** (tr) LWA-Dann Tardif/Corbis. **61** Row 1: (l) Getty Images, (ml) C Squared Studios/Getty Images, (mr) Getty Images, (r) Artville. Row 2: (l) Steve Mason/Getty Images, (ml) Getty Images, (mr) Michael Jang/Getty Images, (r) Jules Frazier/Getty Images. **62** Row 1: (l) John Paul Endress, (m) Stockbyte, (r) Getty Images. Row 2: (l) Getty Images, (m) Digital Stock, (r) Paul Beard/Getty Images. **63** Row 1: (l) Digital Stock, (ml) Leonard de Selva/Corbis, (mr) Artville, (r) Getty Images. Row 2: (l) Getty Images, (ml) Digital Stock, (mr) Siede Preis/Getty Images, (r) Phillippa Lewis/Edivice/Corbis. **66** (tr) Gabriela Median/SuperStock. **67** (tr) Dany Leham/Corbis. **69** (tr) Cartesia. **72** (tl) Courtesy of Brown Publishing Network, (tr) Daivd Young Wolff/Getty Images, (ml, mr) Courtesy of Brown Publishing Network. **73** Row 1: (l, r) Ronnie Kaufman/Corbis. Row 2: (l, m) Liz Garza Williams, (r) Michael Newman/PhotoEdit. Row 3: (l, m, r) Liz Garza Williams. **78** Row 1: (l) Jon Smyth/SuperStock, (m) Artville, (r) Barbara Penoyar/Getty Images. Row 2: (l) Carl & Ann Purcell/Corbis, (m) John Paul Endress, (r) Digital Stock. Row 3: (m) Carl & Ann Purcell/Corbis, (r) John Paul Endress. **79** (l) Getty

Images, (ml, mr) Liz Garza Williams, (r) Stockbyte/Getty Images. **80** (tl) Getty Images, (tc) John Paul Endress, (tr) John Foster/Photo Researchers, Inc., (ml) John Paul Endress, (mc) Stockbyte, (mr) Image Club, (bc) John Paul Endress, (br) Stockbyte. **81** Row 1: (l, ml) Artville, (mr) Digital Studios, (r) Getty Images. Row 2: (l) Leonard de Selva/Corbis, (ml) Artville, (mr) New Century Graphics, (r) Michael Newman/PhotoEdit. **82** (tl) Liz Garza Williams. **83** (tl) Getty Images, (br) Jeff Greenberg/PhotoEdit. **84** (tr) Charlie Dass/SuperStock. **85** (tr) Sal Maimone/SuperStock. **90** (tl) David Young-Wolff/PhotoEdit, (ml) Michale Newman/PhotoEdit, (mr) Tony Freeman/PhotoEdit, (bl) Michael Newman/PhotoEdit, (br) John Lawlor/Getty Images. **91** (tl, tr, ml, mr) Liz Garza Williams. **95** Row 1: (l) Metaphotos, (ml) Robert Daly/Getty Images, (mr) C Squared Studios/Getty Images, (r) Artville. Row 2: (l) Spike Mafford/Getty Images, (ml) John Paul Endress, (mr) Getty Images, (r) Image Library. Row 3: (m) Artville, (r) Spike Mafford/Getty Images. **96** Row 1: (l) Stephen Simpson/Getty Images, (ml) Artville, (mr, r) Getty Images. Row 2: (l) Getty Images, (ml) Artville, (mr) Roderick Chen/Super/Stock, (r) John Paul Endress. Row 3: (m) Stephen Simpson/Getty Images, (r) Getty Images. Row 4: (m) Artville, (r) Getty Images. **97** Row 1: (l) Ryan McVay/getty Images, (ml) John Paul Endress, (mr) Roderick Chen/SuperStock, (r) Michale Dunn/Corbis. Row 2: (l) Getty Images, (ml) Liz Garza Williams, (mr) Nancy R. Cohen/Getty Images, (r) Metaphotos. Row 3: (m) Getty Images, (r) Nancy R. Cohen/Getty Images. Row 4: (m) Roderick Chen/SuperStock, (r) John Paul Endress. **98** Row 1: (l) Liz Garza Williams, (ml, mr) Getty Images, (r) James Forte/Getty Images. Row 2: (l) Getty Images, (ml) Artville, (mr) Liz Garza Williams, (r) Getty Images. **99** (tl) Liz Garza Williams. **101** (tr) Digital Vision/Alamy. **102** (tr) Tony Freeman/PhotoEdit. **108** (ml, bl) Liz Garza Williams. **109** (tl) Getty Images. Row 1: (l) Digital Stock, (ml) Liz Garza Williams, (mr) Richard Hutchings/PhotoEdit, (r) Brian Bailey/Getty Images. **113** Row 1: (l, m) Getty Images, (r) Liz Garza Williams, Row 2: (l) Liz Garza Williams, (m) Artville, (r) Bruce Hands/Getty Images. Row 3: (m) Getty Images, (r) Liz Garza Williams. **114** Row 1: (l) Getty Images, (ml) Artville, (m)

©Zdorov Kirill Vladimirovich/Shutterstock, (mr) Jerry Tobias/Corbis, (r) Liz Garza Williams. Row 2: (l) Bruce Hands/Getty Images, (ml, m) Getty Images, (mr) PurestockSuperStock, (r) Felicia Martinez/PhotoEdit. Row 3: (l) ©Creatas/Jupiterimages, (ml) Joe Munroe/Photo Researchers, (m) Don Mason/Brand X/Jupiter Images, (mr) Digital Stock, (r) Corel. Row 4: (m) SuperStock, (r) Ariel Skelley/Corbis. **115** Row 1: (l) Getty Images, (ml) Roderick Chen/SuperStock, (mr) David Young-Wolff/PhotoEdit, (r) Corel. Row 2: (l) Getty Images, (ml) Okapia Frankfurt/Photo Researchers Inc., (mr) Digital Stock, (r) Nancy R. Cohen/Getty Images. Row 3: (m) Roderick Chen/SuperStock, (r) Getty Images. **116** Row 1: (l) John Paul Endress, (ml) Don Mason/Brand X/Jupiter Images, (mr) Ariel Skelley/Corbis, (r) Bruce Hands/Getty Images. Row 2: (l) Digital Stock, (ml) Siede Preis/Getty Images, (mr) Warren Bolster/Getty Images, (r) Pat O'Hara/Corbis. **117** (tl) S. Nielson/Bruce Coleman. **118** (tl) Dana White/PhotoEdit, (br) Steve Mason/Getty Images. **119** (tr) NASA Goddard Space Flight Center. **120** (r) Adastra/Getty Images. **124, 125, 126** (all) Liz Garza Williams. **135** (tr) Comstock Images/Alamy. **136** (tr) Radius Images/Alamy. **141** (tl) Deborah Davis/PhotoEdit, (ml) Tony Freeman/PhotoEdit, (bl) Courtesy of Lawrence Migdale Photography. **142** (tl) Craig Lovell/Corbis, (tr) AFP/Getty Images. **143** (tl) Dean Conger/Corbis, (ml) Getty Images, (mr) Karen Moskowitz/Corbis, (bl) Earl & Nazima Kowall/Corbis, (br) Charles & Josette Lenars/Corbis. **147** (tl) Ariel Skelly/Corbis, (ml, bl) Getty Images. **149** (tr) Richard Cummins/SuperStock. **150** (tr) Photo Japan/Alamy.

Illustrations

F8, F9 Liisa Chauncey Guida. **F26** Chi Chung. **2-4, 14, 21-22, 26** Judith DuFour. **31** Norm Bendell. **38-39, 48** Judith DuFour. **54, 56-57** Maurie Manning, **64** Norm Bendell. **65** Maurie Manning. **71, 89, 110, 106-108** Judith DuFour. **114** Alex von Dallwitz. **127, 131-132** Maurie Manning. **133** Norm Bendell. **134, 140** Judith DuFour. **155-178** Dick Smolinski. **179-182** Lee Woolry. **183-186** Dick Smolinski. **187-190** Den Schofield.